THE MASTERPLAN

SONY MUSIC PUBLISHING

Exclusive Distributors:
Music Sales Limited
8/9 Frith Street, London W1V 5TZ, England.
Music Sales Pty Limited
120 Rothschild Avenue, Rosebery, NSW 2018, Australia.

Order No. AM954547
ISBN 0-7119-7275-3
This book © Copyright 1998 by Sony Music Publishing.

Music arranged by Arthur Dick.
New engravings by Paul Ewers Music Design.
Printed in the United Kingdom by Caligraving Limited, Thetford, Norfolk.

Your Guarantee of Quality:
As publishers, we strive to produce every book to the highest commercial standards.
The music has been freshly engraved and, whilst endeavouring to retain the original
running order of the recorded album, the book has been carefully designed to minimise
awkward page turns and to make playing from it a real pleasure.
Particular care has been given to specifying acid-free, neutral-sized paper made from
pulps which have not been elemental chlorine bleached.
This pulp is from farmed sustainable forests and was produced with special regard for the environment.
Throughout, the printing and binding have been planned to ensure a sturdy, attractive
publication which should give years of enjoyment.
If your copy fails to meet our high standards, please inform us and we will gladly replace it.

Music Sales' complete catalogue describes thousands of titles and is available in full colour
sections by subject, direct from Music Sales Limited.
Please state your areas of interest and send a cheque/postal order for £1.50 for postage to:
Music Sales Limited, Newmarket Road, Bury St. Edmunds, Suffolk IP33 3YB.

GUITAR TABLATURE EXPLAINED

Guitar music can be notated three different ways: on a musical stave, in tablature, and in rhythm slashes

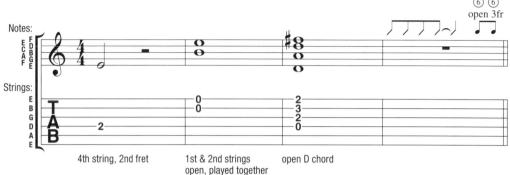

RHYTHM SLASHES are written above the stave. Strum chords in the rhythm indicated. Round noteheads indicate single notes.

THE MUSICAL STAVE shows pitches and rhythms and is divided by lines into bars. Pitches are named after the first seven letters of the alphabet.

TABLATURE graphically represents the guitar fingerboard. Each horizontal line represents a string, and each number represents a fret.

4th string, 2nd fret

1st & 2nd strings open, played together

open D chord

Definitions for special guitar notation

SEMI-TONE BEND: Strike the note and bend up a semi-tone (1/2 step).

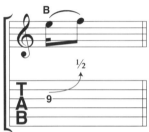

WHOLE-TONE BEND: Strike the note and bend up a whole-tone (whole step).

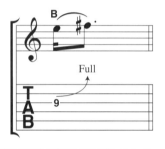

GRACE NOTE BEND: Strike the note and bend as indicated. Play the first note as quickly as possible.

QUARTER-TONE BEND: Strike the note and bend up a 1/4 step.

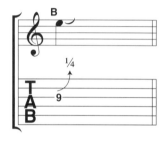

BEND & RELEASE: Strike the note and bend up as indicated, then release back to the original note.

COMPOUND BEND & RELEASE: Strike the note and bend up and down in the rhythm indicated.

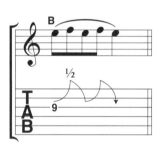

PRE-BEND: Bend the note as indicated, then strike it.

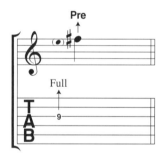

PRE-BEND & RELEASE: Bend the note as indicated. Strike it and release the note back to the original pitch.

UNISON BEND: Strike the two notes simultaneously and bend the lower note up to the pitch of the higher.

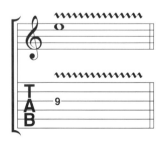

BEND & RESTRIKE: Strike the note and bend as indicated then restrike the string where the symbol occurs.

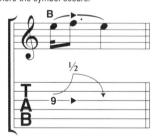

BEND, HOLD AND RELEASE: Same as bend and release but hold the bend for the duration of the tie.

BEND AND TAP: Bend the note as indicated and tap the higher fret while still holding the bend.

VIBRATO: The string is vibrated by rapidly bending and releasing the note with the fretting hand.

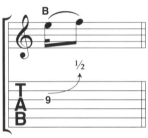

HAMMER-ON: Strike the first (lower) note with one finger, then sound the higher note (on the same string) with another finger by fretting it without picking.

PULL-OFF: Place both fingers on the notes to be sounded, Strike the first note and without picking, pull the finger off to sound the second (lower) note.

LEGATO SLIDE (GLISS): Strike the first note and then slide the same fret-hand finger up or down to the second note. The second note is not struck.

NOTE: The speed of any bend is indicated by the music notation and tempo.

SHIFT SLIDE (GLISS & RESTRIKE): Same as legato slide, except the second note is struck.

TRILL: Very rapidly alternate between the notes indicated by continuously hammering on and pulling off.

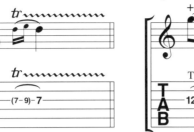

TAPPING: Hammer ("tap") the fret indicated with the pick-hand index or middle finger and pull off to the note fretted by the fret hand.

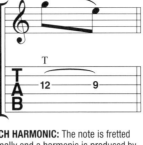

PICK SCRAPE: The edge of the pick is rubbed down (or up) the string, producing a scratchy sound.

MUFFLED STRINGS: A percussive sound is produced by laying the fret hand across the string(s) without depressing, and striking them with the pick hand.

NATURAL HARMONIC: Strike the note while the fret-hand lightly touches the string directly over the fret indicated.

Harm.

PINCH HARMONIC: The note is fretted normally and a harmonic is produced by adding the edge of the thumb or the tip of the index finger of the pick hand to the normal pick attack.

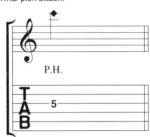

P.H.

HARP HARMONIC: The note is fretted normally and a harmonic is produced by gently resting the pick hand's index finger directly above the indicated fret (in parentheses) while the pick hand's thumb or pick assists by plucking the appropriate string.

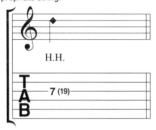

H.H.

PALM MUTING: The note is partially muted by the pick hand lightly touching the string(s) just before the bridge.

P.M.

RAKE: Drag the pick across the strings indicated with a single motion.

rake

TREMOLO PICKING: The note is picked as rapidly and continuously as possible.

ARPEGGIATE: Play the notes of the chord indicated by quickly rolling them from bottom to top.

SWEEP PICKING: Rhythmic downstroke and/or upstroke motion across the strings.

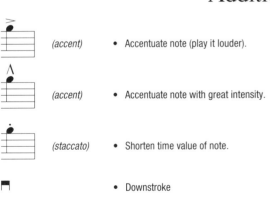

VIBRATO DIVE BAR AND RETURN: The pitch of the note or chord is dropped a specific number of steps (in rhythm) then returned to the original pitch.

w/bar

VIBRATO BAR SCOOP: Depress the bar just before striking the note, then quickly release the bar.

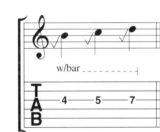

w/bar

VIBRATO BAR DIP: Strike the note and then immediately drop a specific number of steps, then release back to the original pitch.

w/bar

Additional musical definitions

$>$ (accent)	•	Accentuate note (play it louder).
$\wedge$ (accent)	•	Accentuate note with great intensity.
• (staccato)	•	Shorten time value of note.
⊓	•	Downstroke
V	•	Upstroke

D.%. al Coda

D.C. al Fine

tacet

• Go back to the sign (%), then play until the bar marked *To Coda* ⊕ then skip to the section marked ⊕ *Coda*.

• Go back to the beginning of the song and play until the bar marked *Fine* (end).

• Instrument is silent (drops out).

• Repeat bars between signs.

1.	2.

• When a repeated section has different endings, play the first ending only the first time and the second ending only the second time.

NOTE: Tablature numbers in parentheses mean: 1. The note is sustained, but a new articulation (such as hammer on or slide) begins.
2. A note may be fretted but not necessarily played.

ACQUIESCE

WORDS & MUSIC BY NOEL GALLAGHER

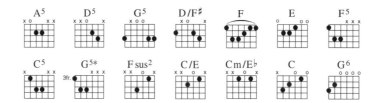

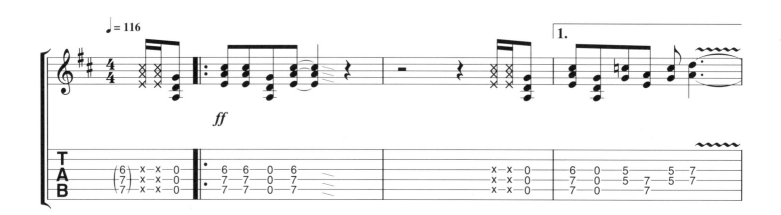

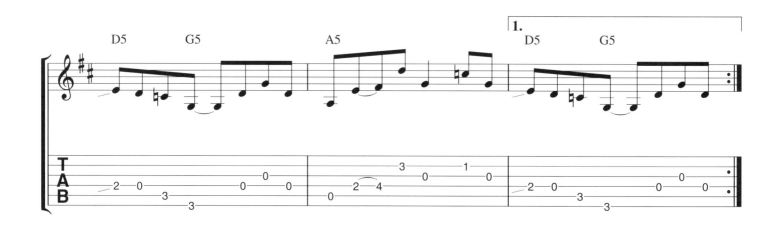

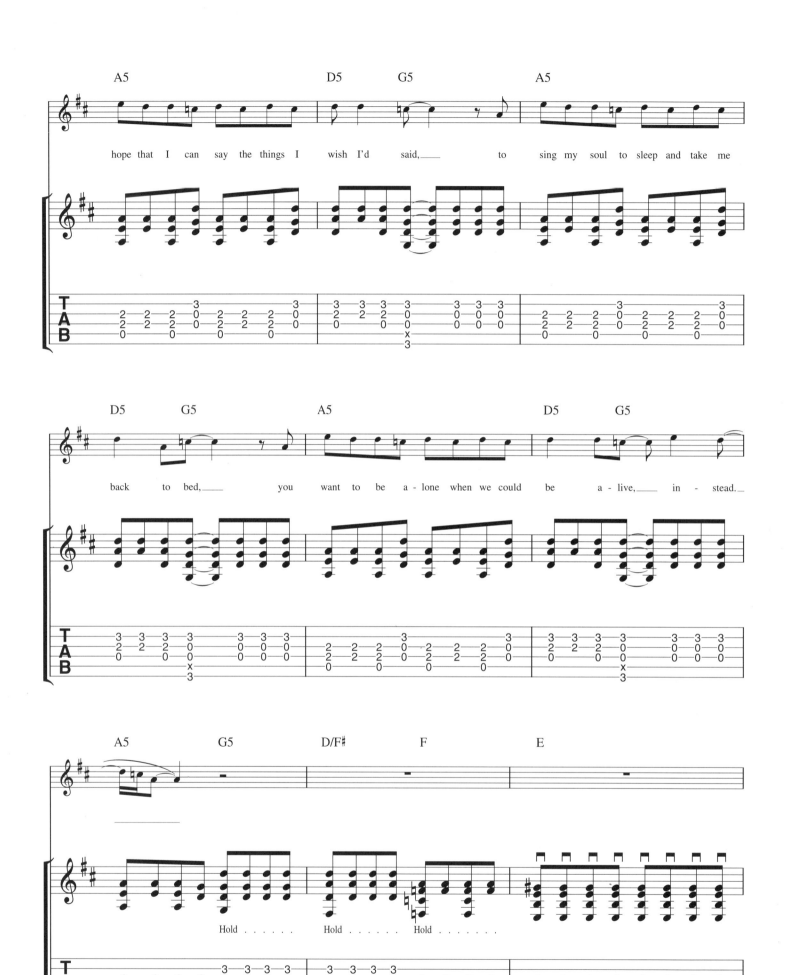

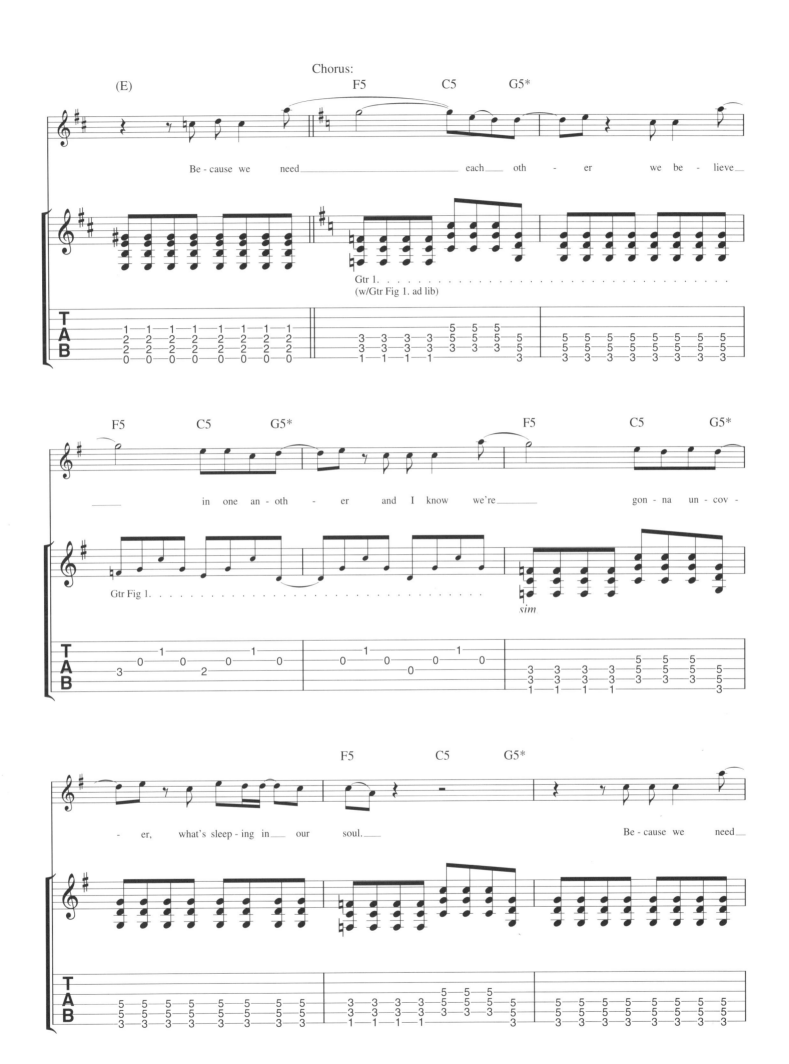

Chorus:

Be - cause we need_____ each___ oth - er we be - lieve_____

in one an - oth - er and I know we're_____ gon - na un - cov-

- er, what's sleep - ing in___ our soul.___ Be - cause we need___

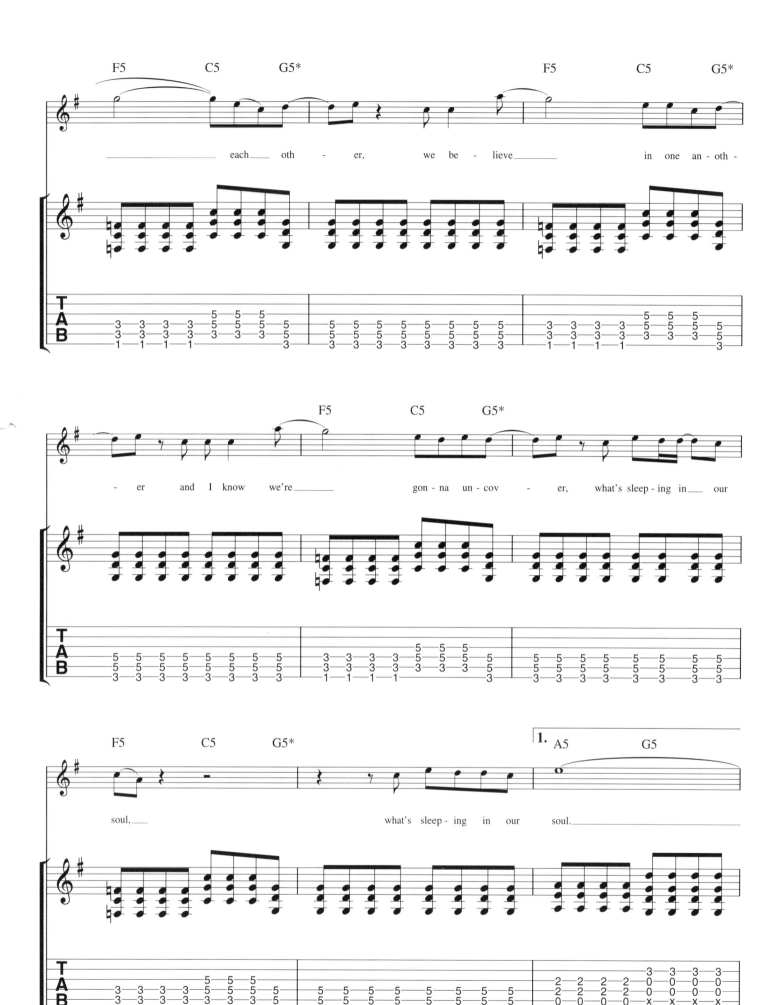

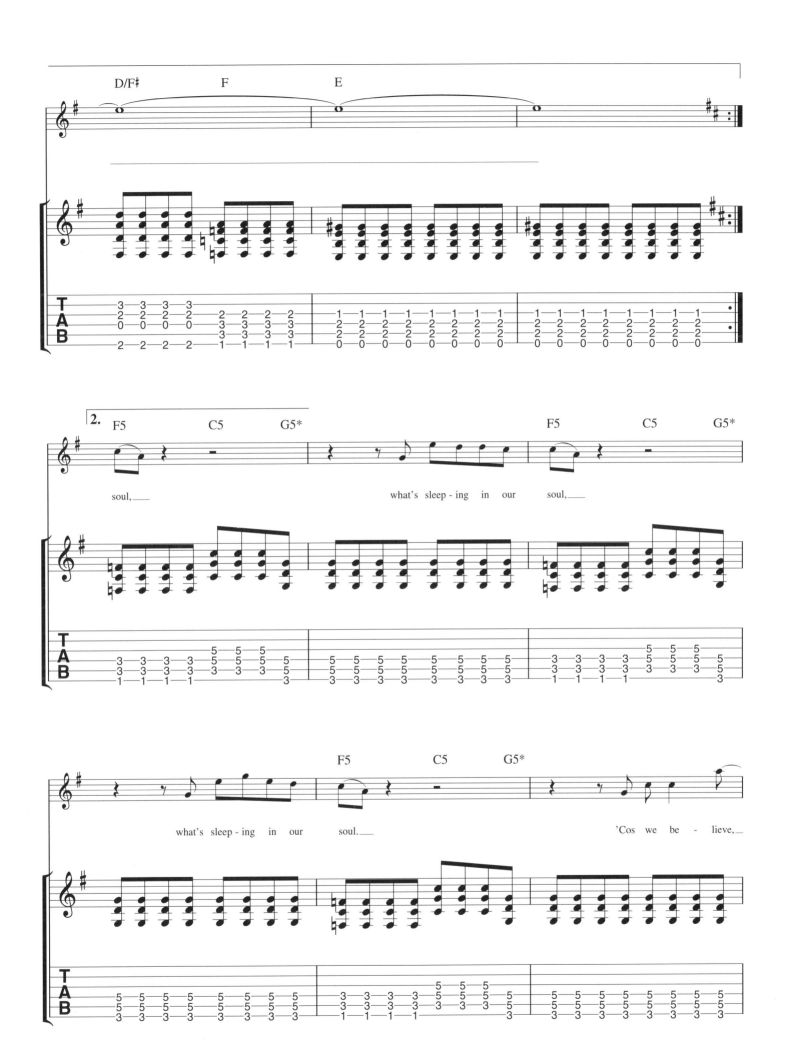

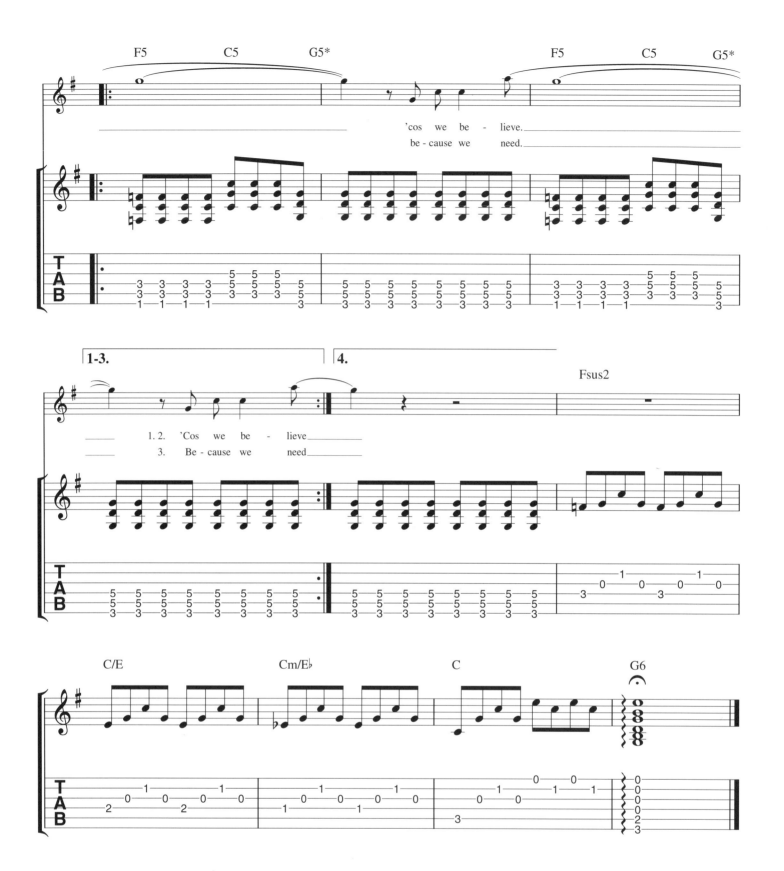

Verse 2:
There are many things that I would like to know
And there are many places that I wish to go
But everything's depending on the way the wind may blow.

I don't know what it is that makes me feel alive
I don't know how to wake the things that sleep inside
I only wanna see the light that shines behind your eyes.

GOING NOWHERE

WORDS & MUSIC BY NOEL GALLAGHER

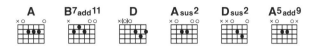

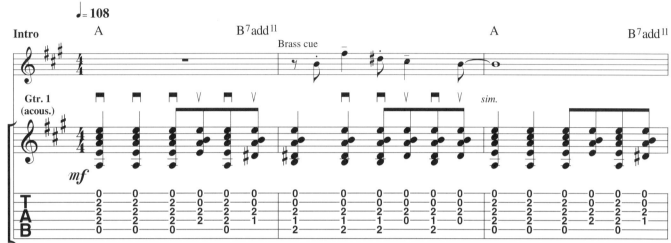

*The pitch of the recording is between A & B♭. (To play in B♭ use Capo at 1st fret.)

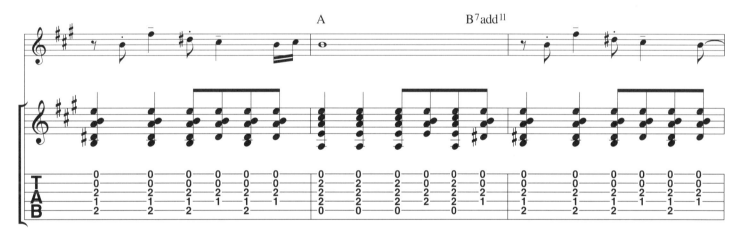

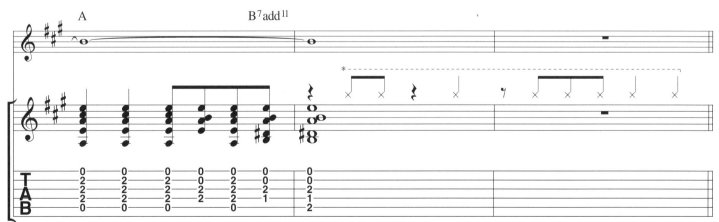

* tap rhythm on body of Gtr.

16

all their ques-tions were si - mi - lar,— the an-swers just— the same.—

Pre-chorus

I'm gon-na get me a mo - tor car, may-be a Ja - gu - ar, may-be a plane—

—— or a day— of fame.—

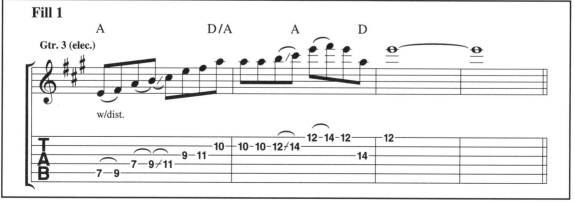

Fill 1

Chorus

Gtr. 1

mf 2° Gtr. 2 plays rhythm sim. to Gtr. 1

sim.

let ring

1.

Gtr. 1: w/Fig. 1

I'm gon-na be a mil-lion-aire, so can you take— me there? Wan-na be wild— —'cause my life's— so tame.— Here am I— go-ing no- -where on— a train,— here am I— grow-ing old- er in— the rain.—

18

UNDERNEATH THE SKY

WORDS & MUSIC BY NOEL GALLAGHER

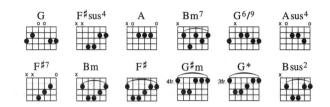

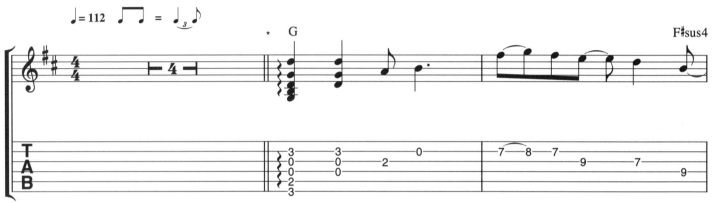

* Composite Gtr part

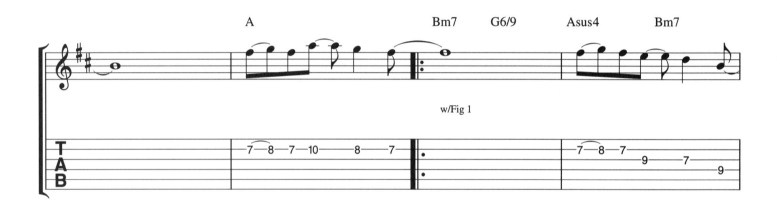

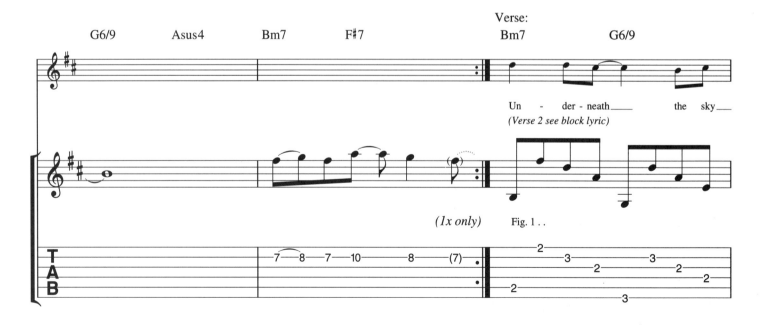

Un - der - neath___ the sky___
(Verse 2 see block lyric)

_____ of red, ___ there's a sto - ry tell - er sleep - ing a - lone._____ He

Hold . . . . . .   Hold .

. . . end Fig 1.

has no face___ and he has_____ no name,___ and his where - a - bouts are sort of un - known.___

(Piano solo on 𝄋)

_____ All___ he needs_____ is his life___ in a suit - case, it be - longs___

Hold . . . . .   Hold . . Hold . . . .   Hold . . . .   Hold . . . .

_to a friend___ of a friend___ and as we drink___ to our-selves___ we'll am-use___

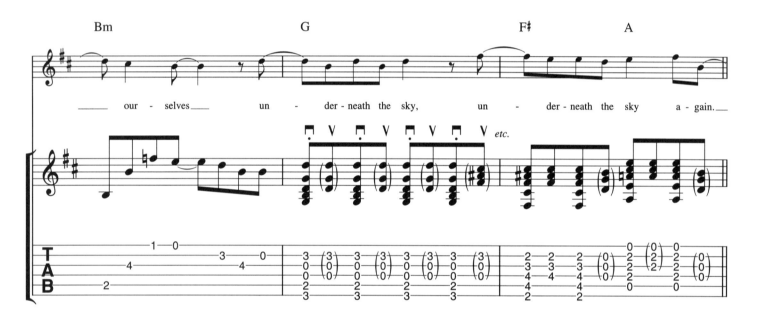

___ our-selves___ un - der-neath the sky, un - der-neath the sky a-gain.___

Chorus:

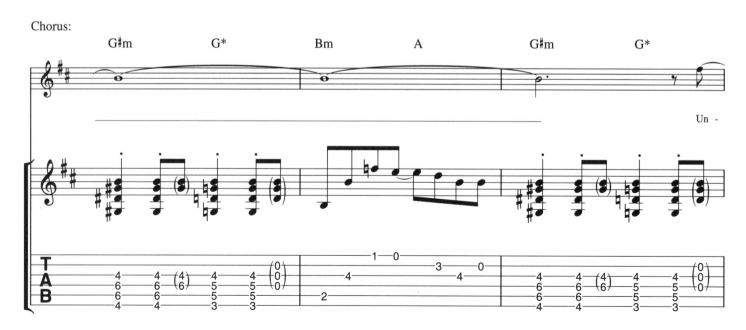

Un -

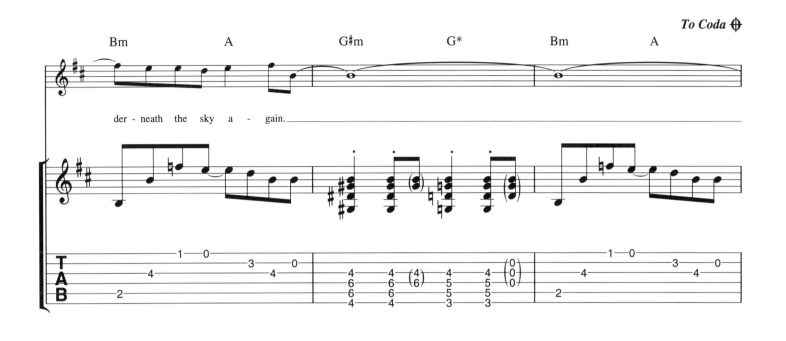

der - neath the sky a - gain.

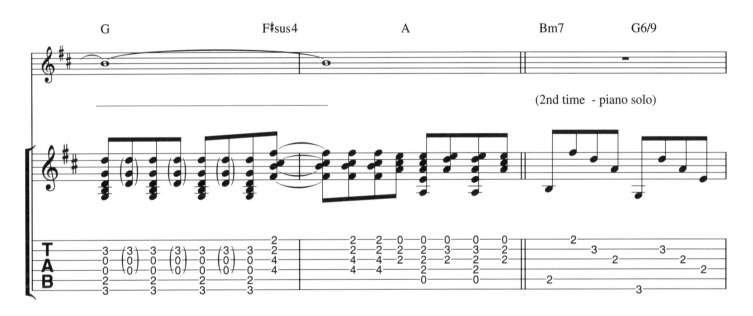

(2nd time - piano solo)

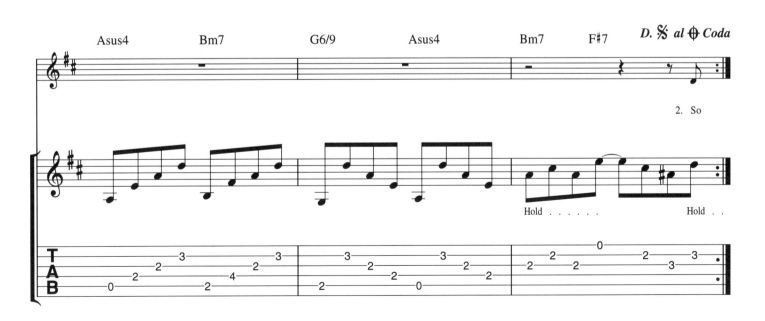

2. So

Hold . . . . . .   Hold . .

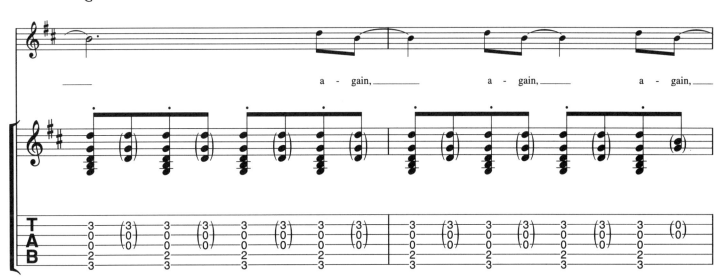

G*

a - gain,_____ a - gain,_____ a - gain,_____

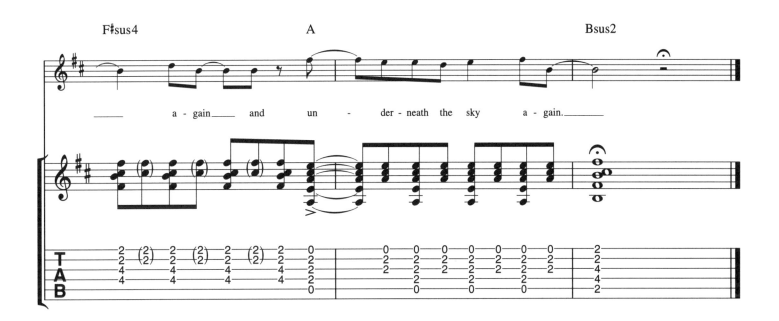

F#sus4   A   Bsus2

_____ a - gain_____ and un - der - neath the sky a - gain._____

Verse 2:   So wish me away to an unknown place
I'm living in a land with no name
I'll be making a start with my brand new heart
Stop me making sense once again.

All we need is our lives in a suitcase
They belong to a friend of a friend
And as we drink to ourselves we'll amuse ourselves
Underneath the sky, underneath the sky again.

Verse 3(𝄋)   *Piano solo*
All we need is our lives in a suitcase
They belong to a friend of a friend
And as we drink to ourselves we'll amuse ourselves
Underneath the sky, underneath the sky again.

TALK TONIGHT

WORDS & MUSIC BY NOEL GALLAGHER

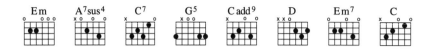

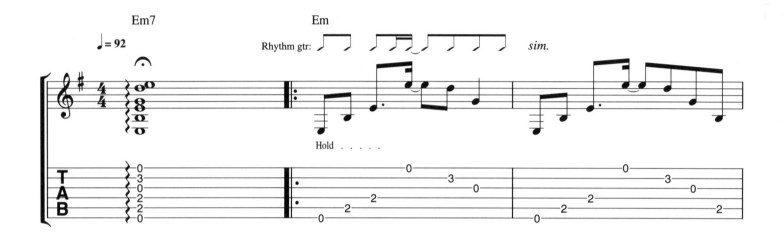

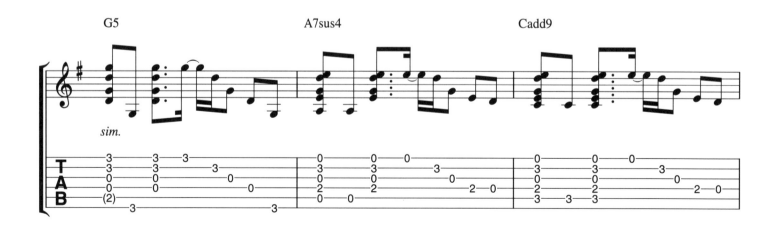

Verse:

Sit - ting on my own, chew - ing on a bone a thou - sand mil - lion miles____
(Verse 2 see block lyric)

Hold . . . . .

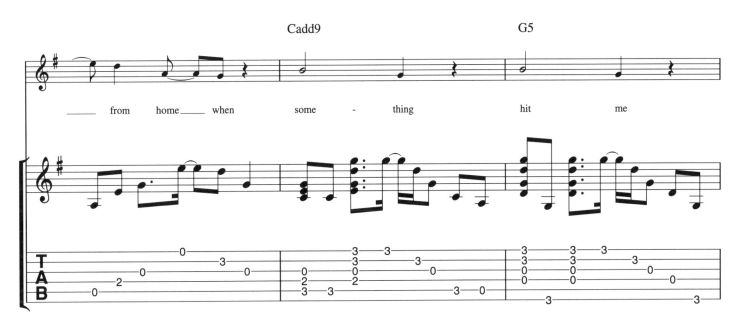

____ from home____ when some - thing hit me

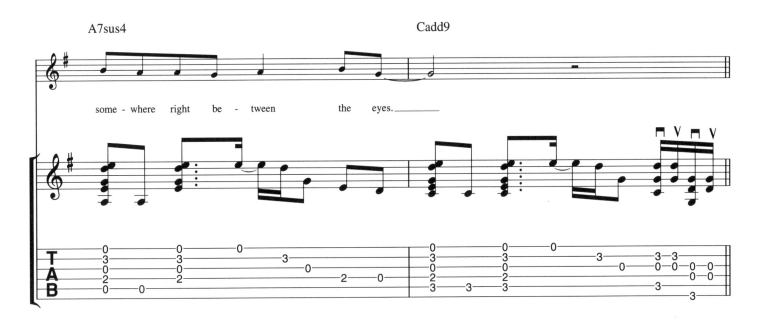

some - where right be - tween the eyes._____

Sleep-ing on a plane, you know___ you can't com-plain, you took___ your last___ chance, once___

Hold . . . . . .

___ a - gain___ I land - ed,

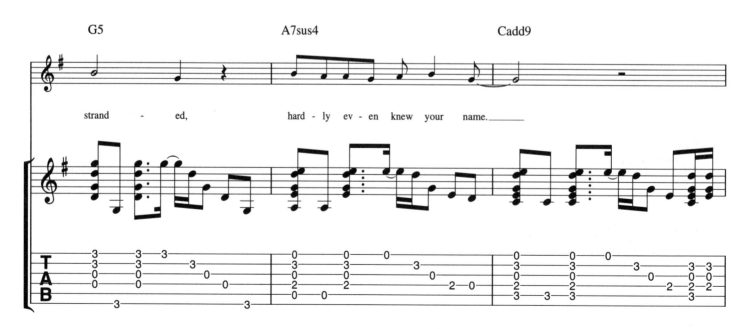

strand - ed, hard - ly ev - en knew your name.___

31

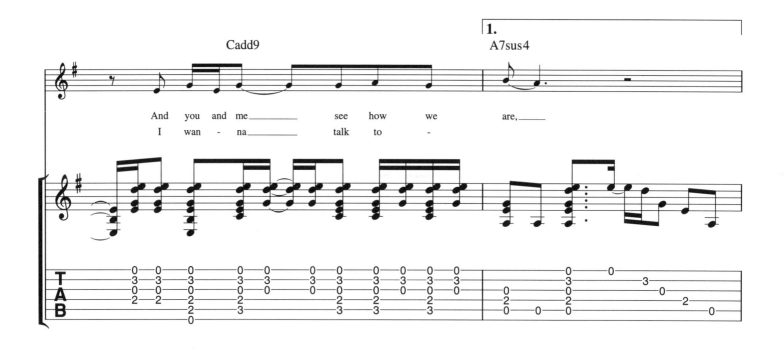

And you and me_____ see how we are,_____
I wan - na_____ talk to -

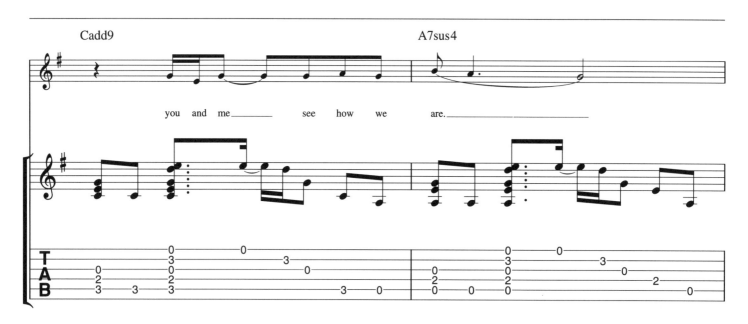

you and me_____ see how we are._____

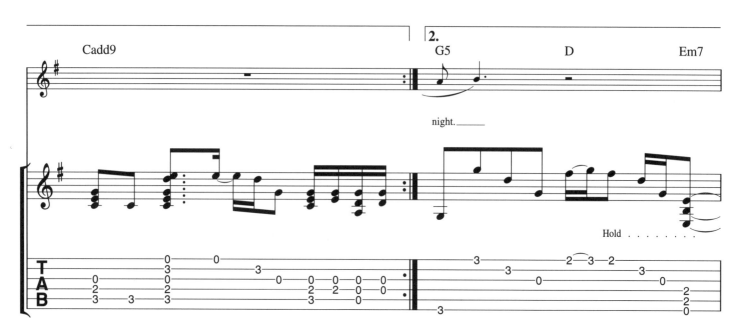

night._____

Hold . . . .

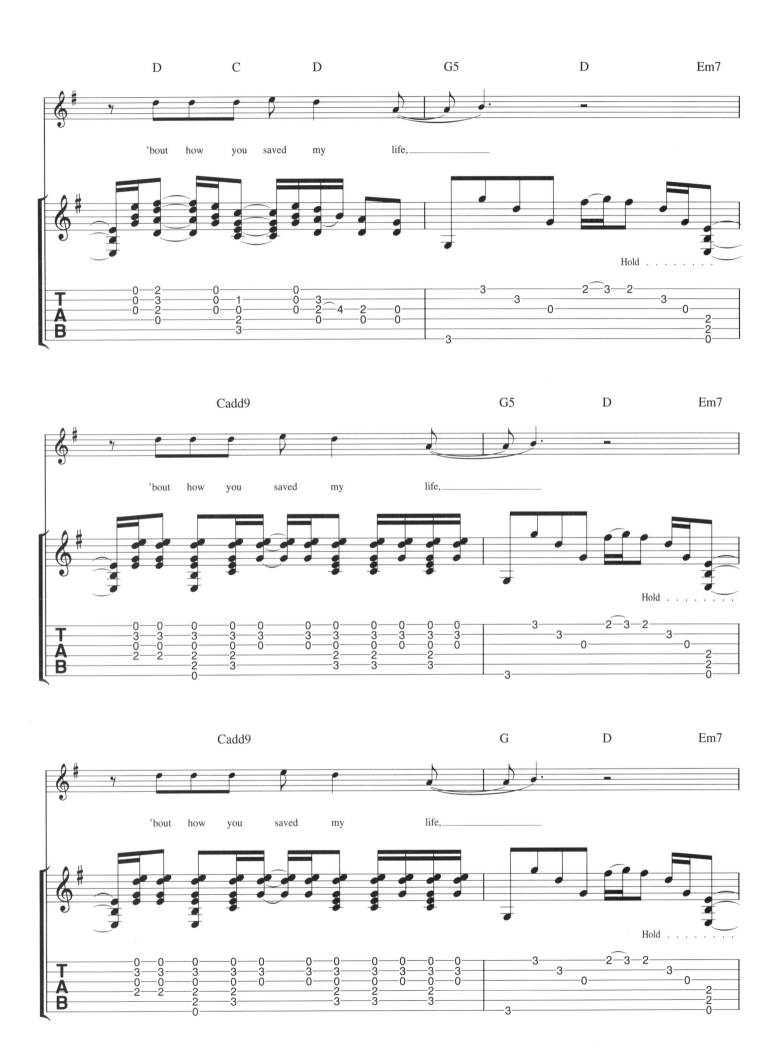

'bout how you saved my life,

'bout how you saved my life,

'bout how you saved my life,

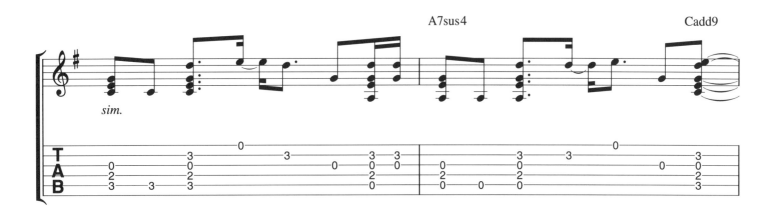

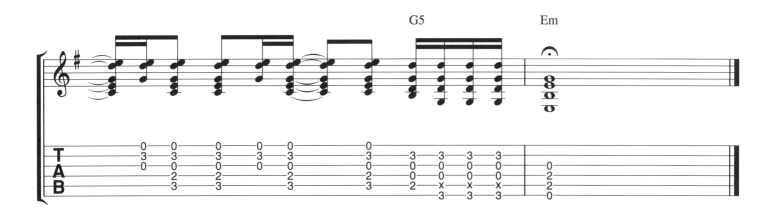

Verse 2: All your dreams are made of strawberry lemonade
And you make sure I eat today
You take me walking
To where you played when you were young.

I'll never say that I won't ever make you cry
And this I'll say I don't know why
I know I'm leaving
But I'll be back another day.

FADE AWAY

WORDS & MUSIC BY NOEL GALLAGHER

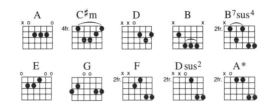

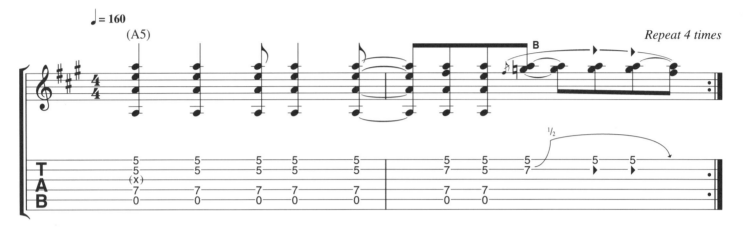

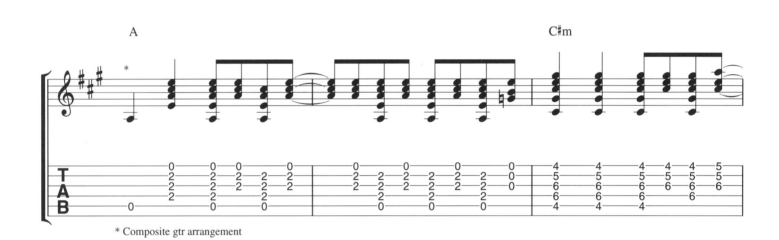

* Composite gtr arrangement

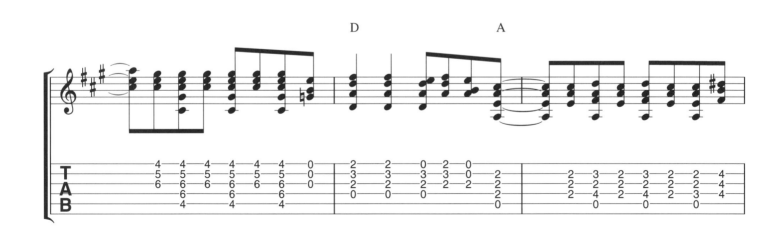

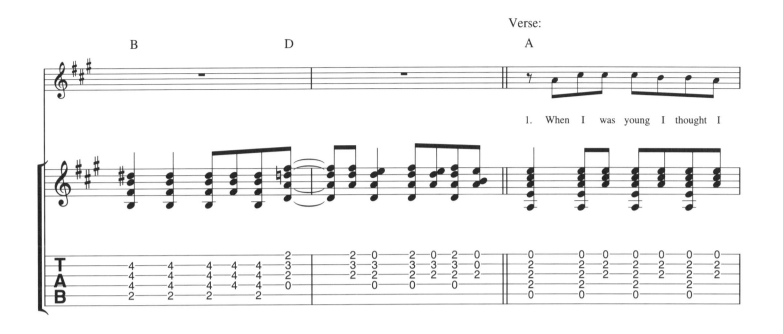

Verse:

1. When I was young I thought I

had my own___ key, I knew ex - act - ly what I want - ed to___ be, now___

___ I'm sure,_____ you've board - ed up ev - 'ry door.___

Verse:

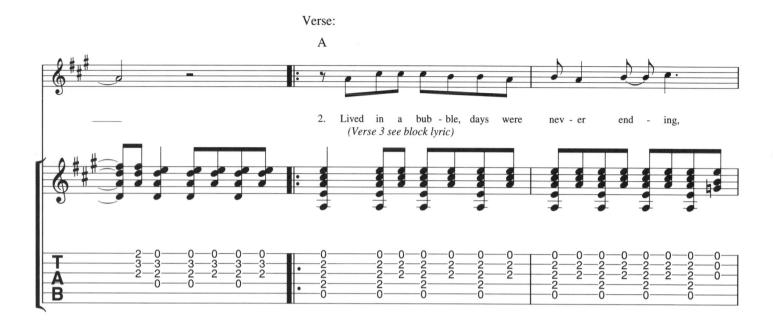

2. Lived in a bub - ble, days were nev - er end - ing,
(Verse 3 see block lyric)

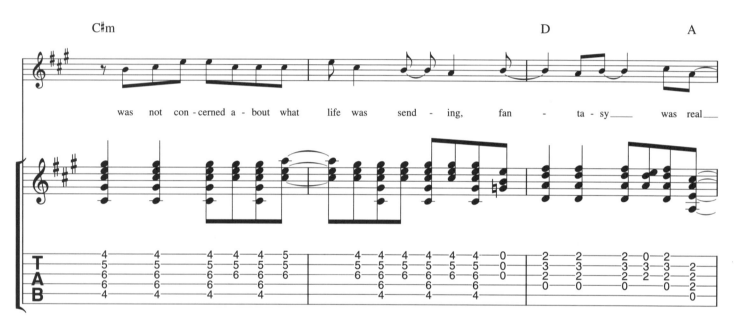

was not con - cerned a - bout what life was send - ing, fan - ta - sy____ was real____

____ now I know much____ a - bout the way I feel.____

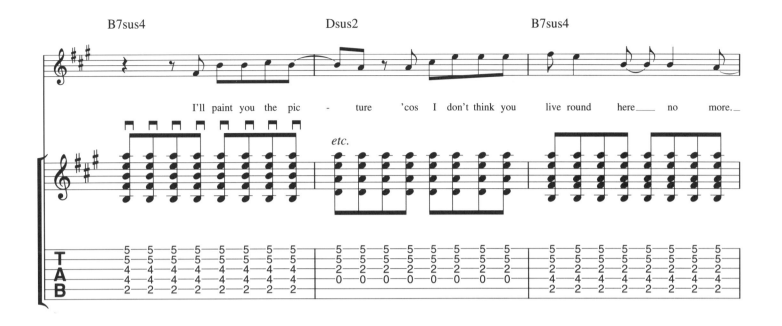

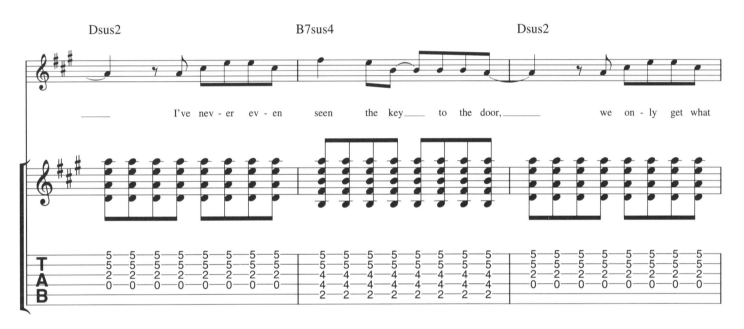

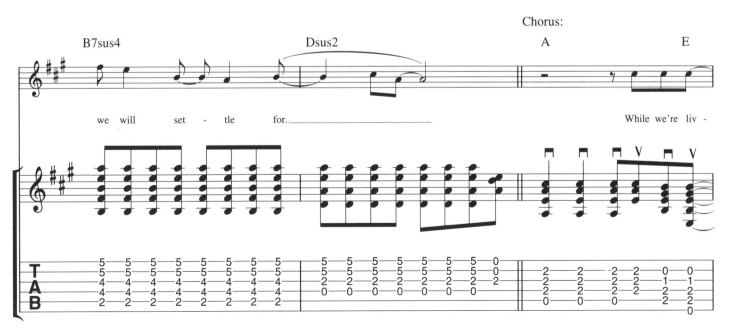

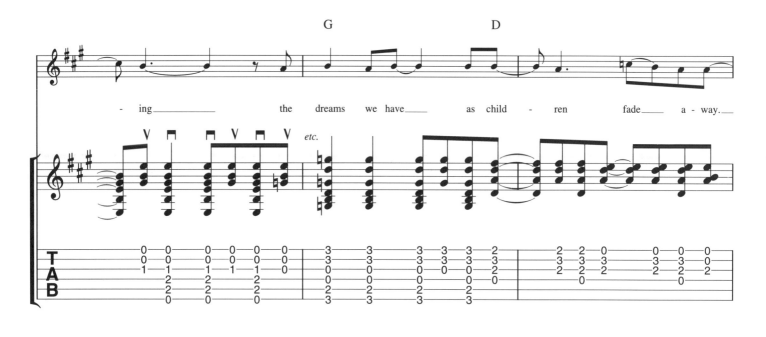

-ing _____ the dreams we have ____ as child - ren fade ____ a - way.

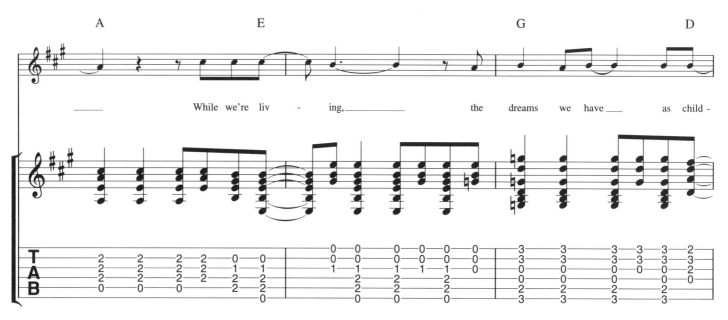

____ While we're liv - ing, ____ the dreams we have ____ as child -

- ren fade ____ a - way. ____ While we're liv - ing, ____ the

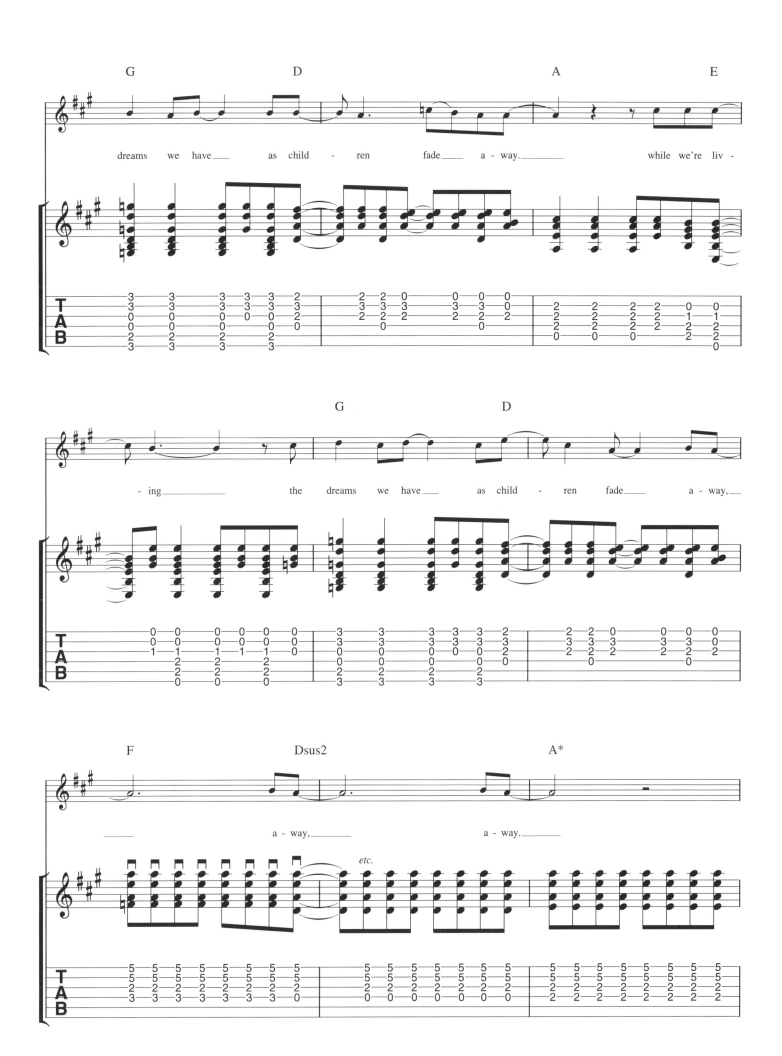

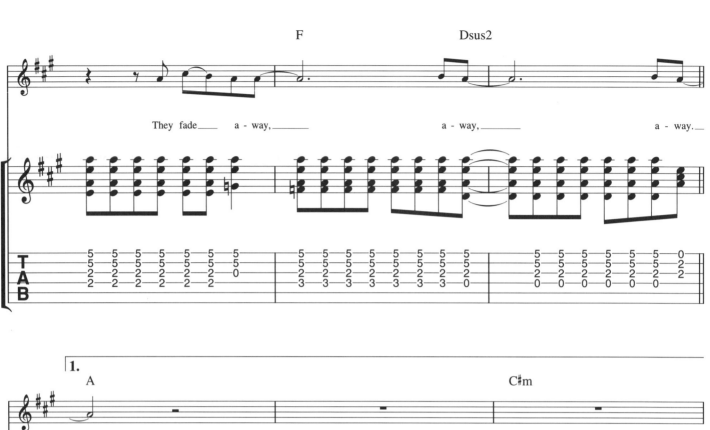

They fade___ a - way,___ a - way,___ a - way.___

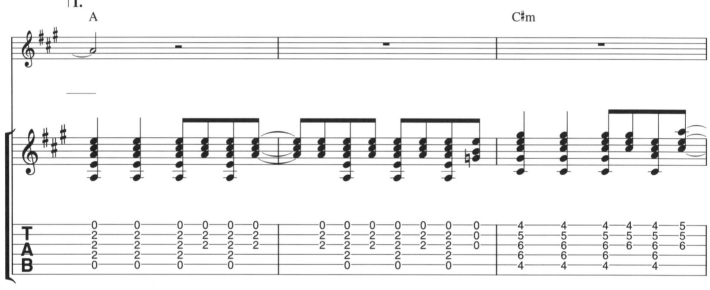

1.

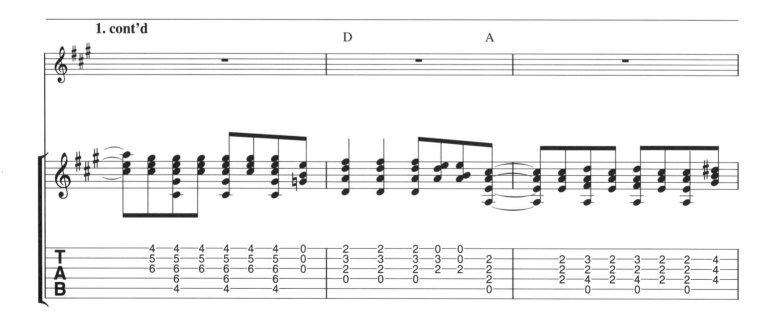

1. cont'd

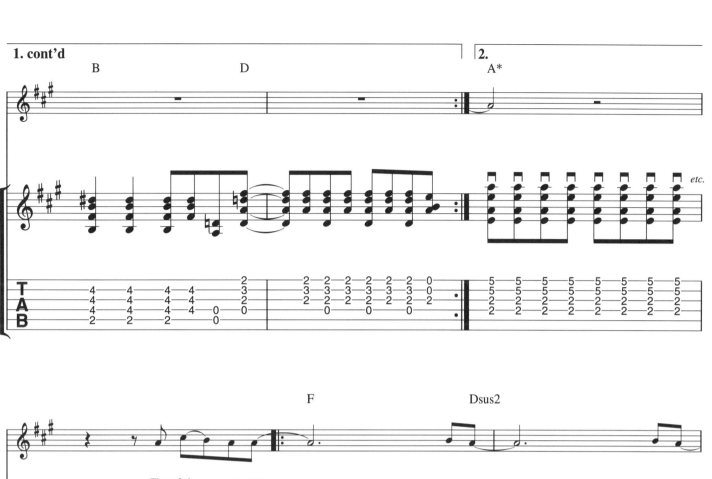

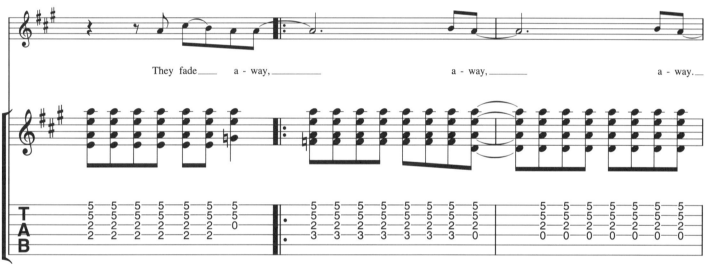

They fade___ a - way,_____ a - way,_____ a - way.___

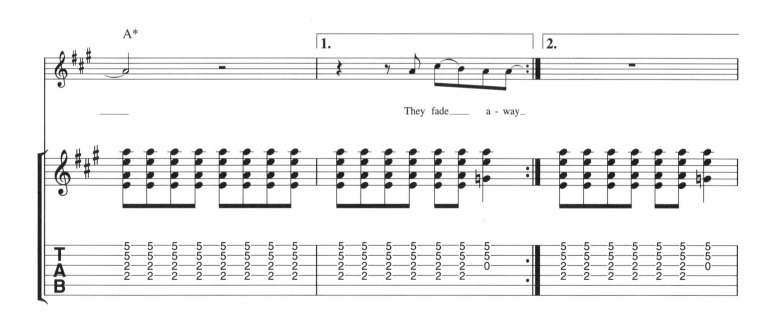

___ They fade___ a - way_

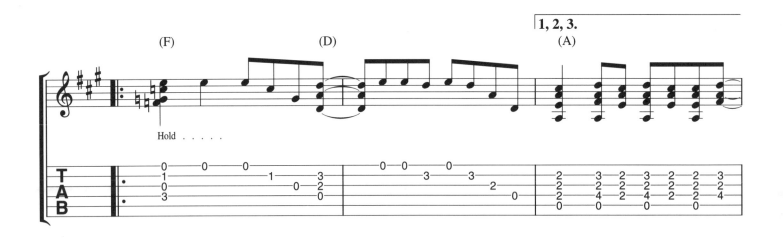

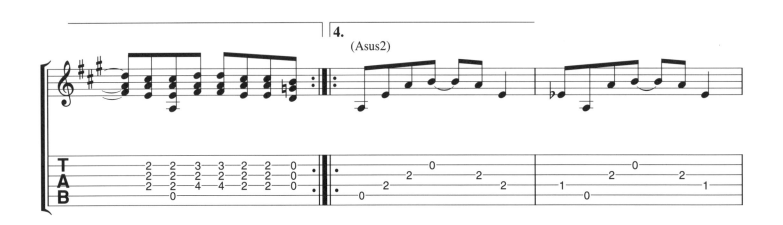

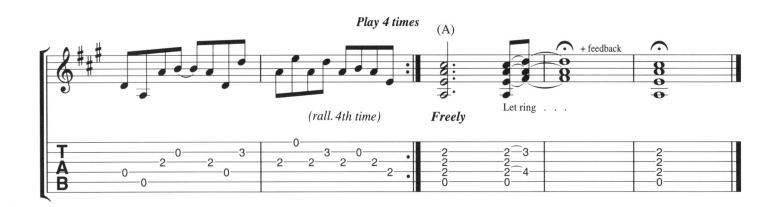

Verse 3:   Now my life has turned another corner
              I think it's only best that I should warn you
              Dream it while you can
              Maybe some day I'll make you understand.

THE SWAMP SONG

WORDS & MUSIC BY NOEL GALLAGHER

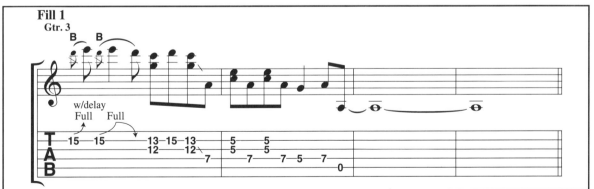

...Fig. 1 ends

Am add⁹   G add⁹/A

Harmonica cue

Gtr. 3 plays chord arpeggios

F add⁹/A   G add⁹/A   A⁵

Solo   A⁵

Gtr. 3

Gtr. 1: w/Fig. 1

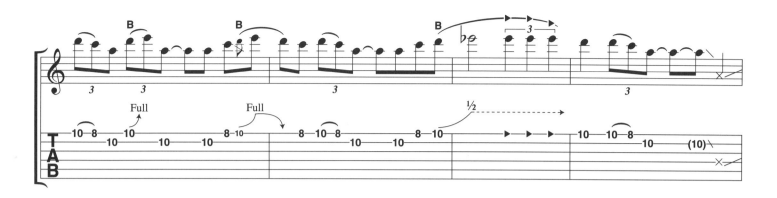

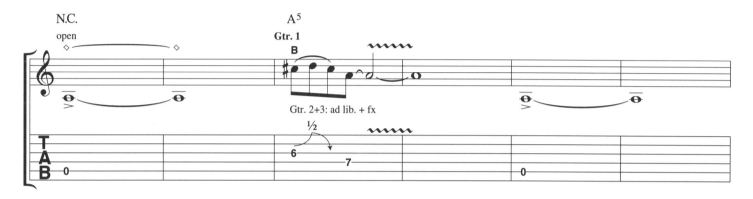

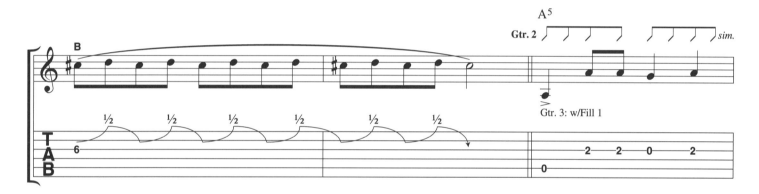

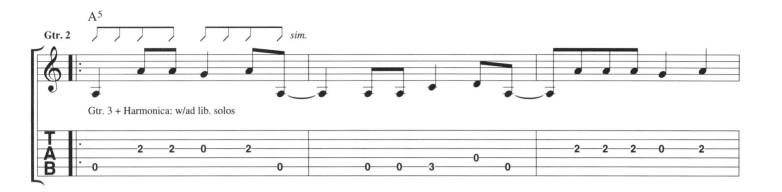

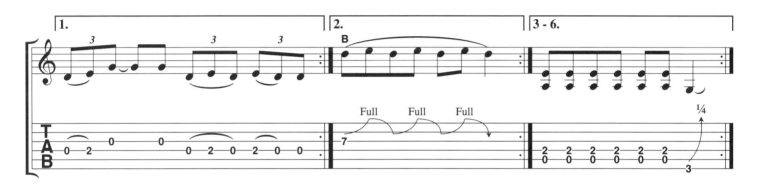

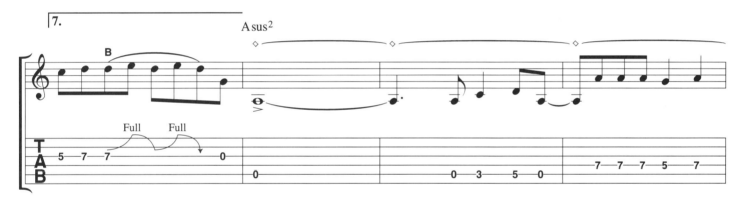

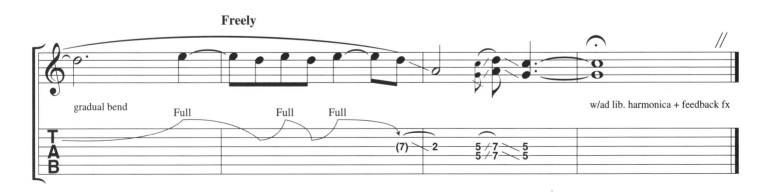

I AM THE WALRUS

WORDS & MUSIC BY JOHN LENNON & PAUL McCARTNEY

1. I am he as you are he as you are me and we are all to - geth -
5. Ex - pert tex - pert, chok - ing smok - ers, don't you think the jok - er laughs at you?—

- er,

See how they run like pigs from a gun, see
See how they smile like pigs in a sty, see

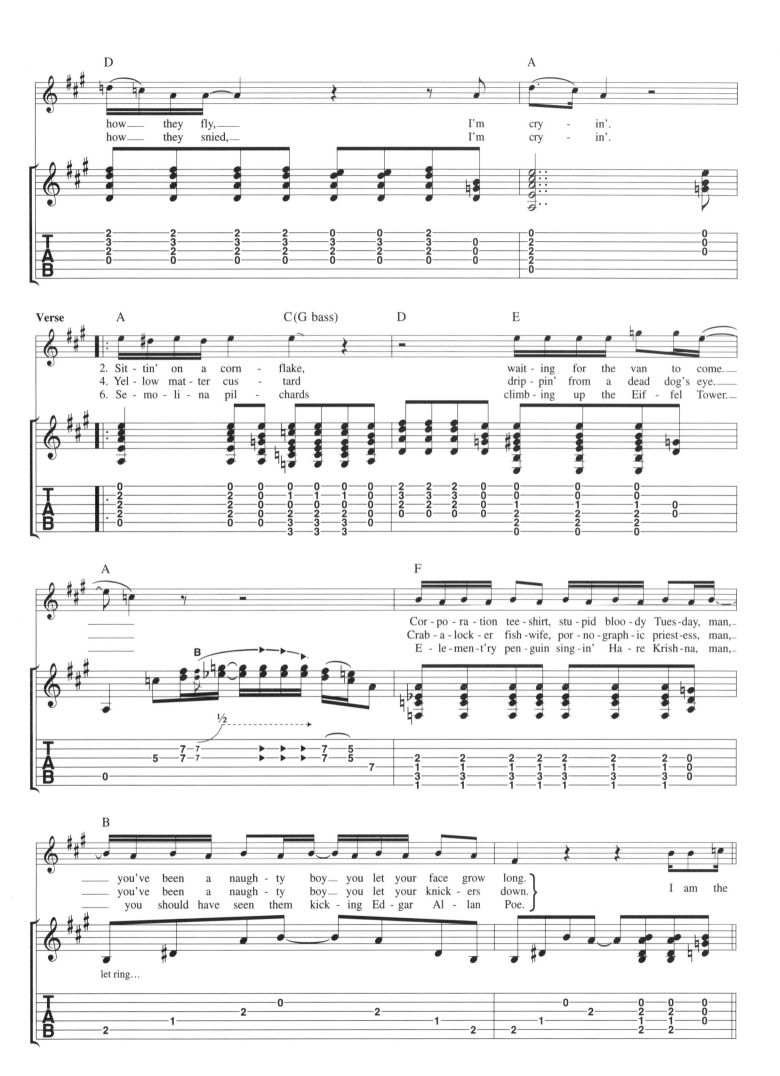

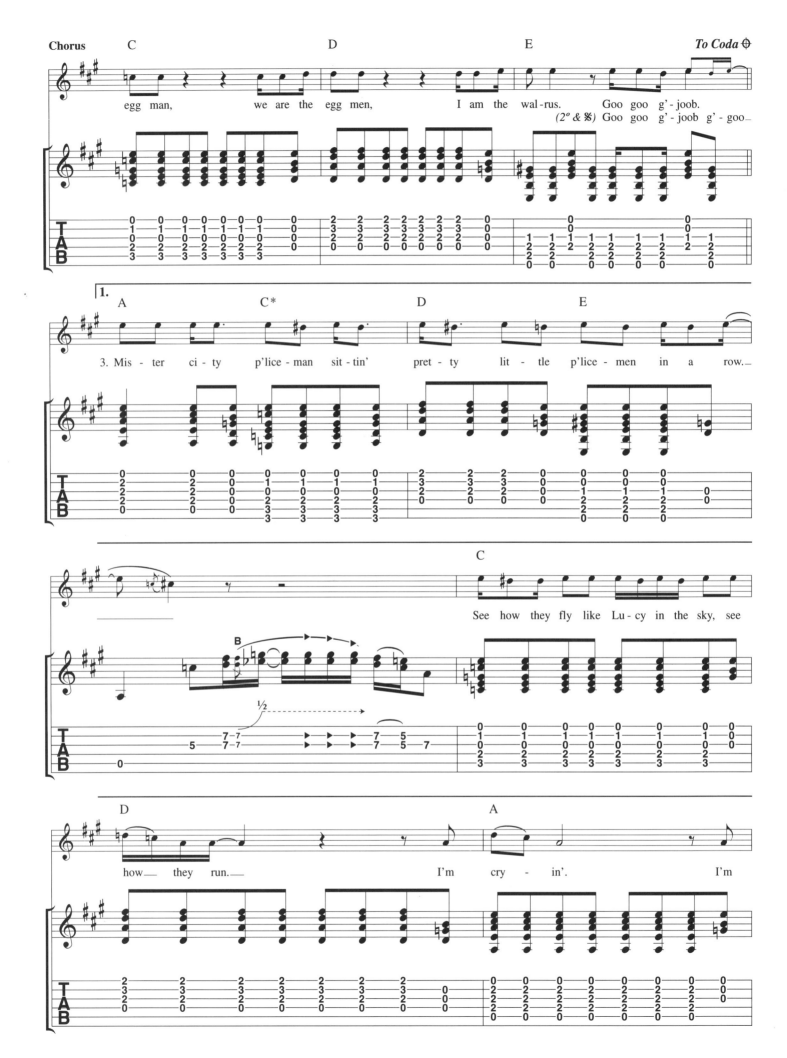

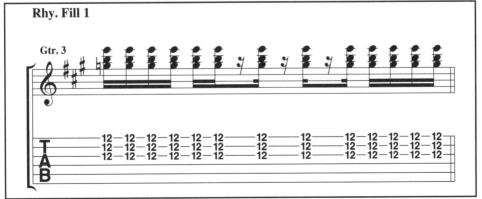

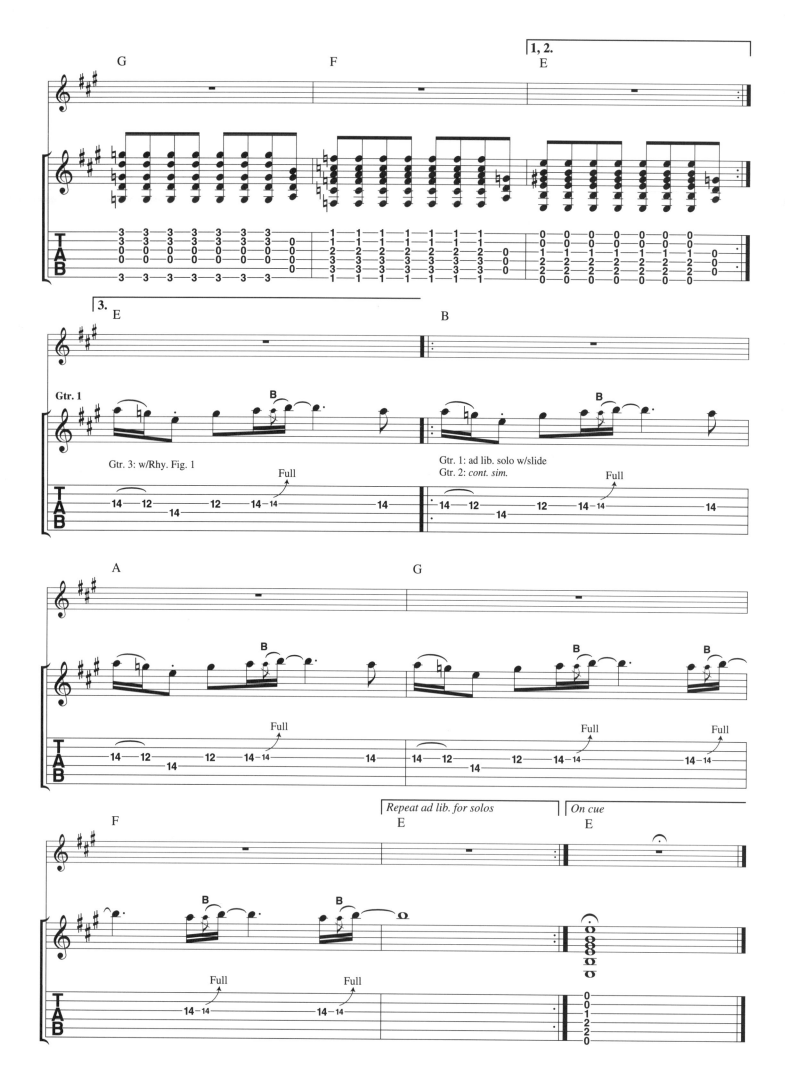

LISTEN UP

WORDS & MUSIC BY NOEL GALLAGHER

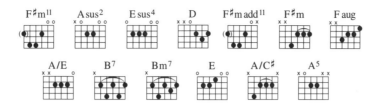

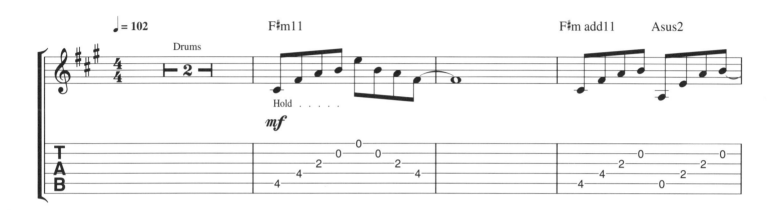

Verse:

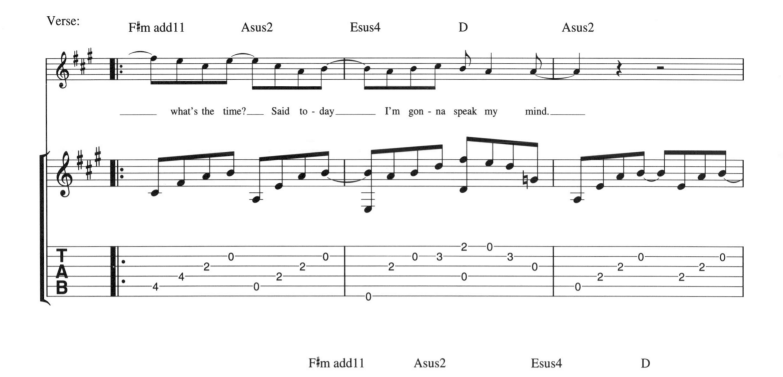

_____ what's the time?____ Said to - day _____ I'm gon - na speak my mind._____

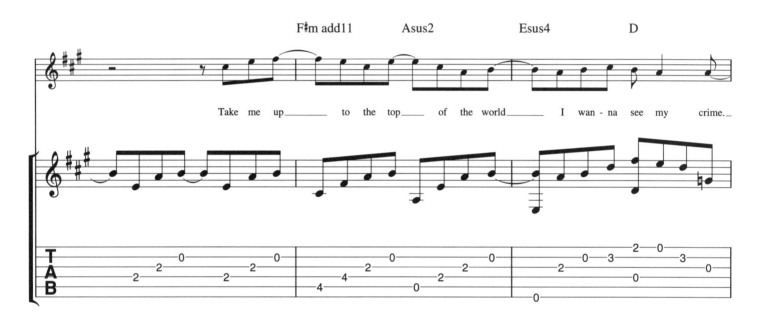

Take me up_____ to the top_____ of the world_____ I wan - na see my crime.__

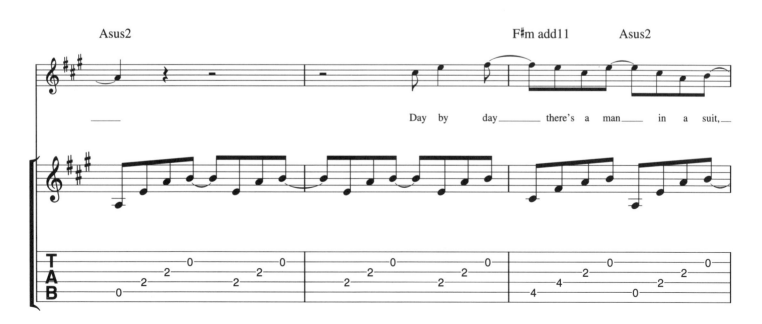

_____ Day by day_____ there's a man____ in a suit,__

who's gon-na make you   pay_____   for   the thoughts_

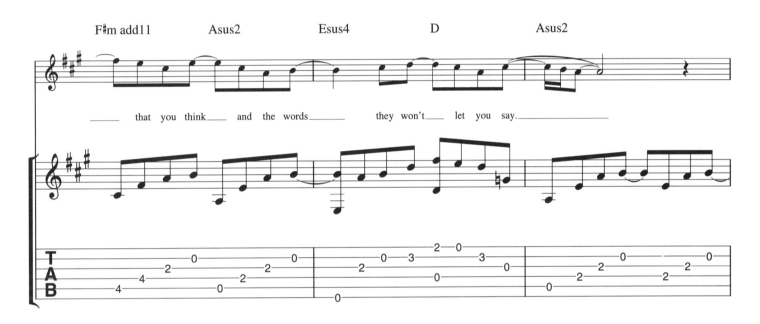

_____   that   you think____   and   the words_____   they won't____   let   you   say._____

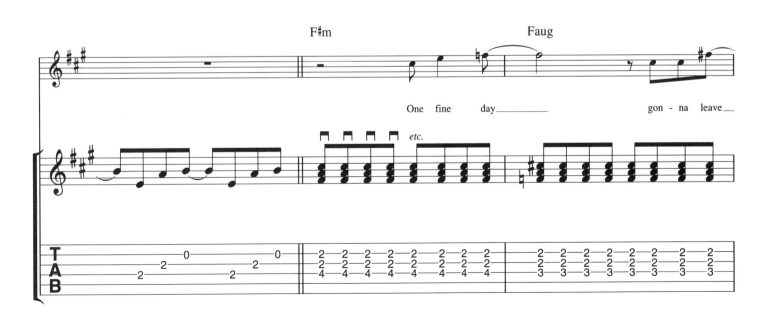

One   fine   day_____   gon - na   leave___

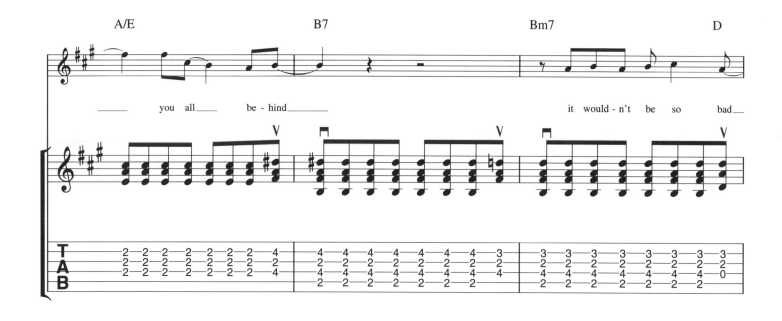

you all____ be - hind_____ it would - n't be so bad__

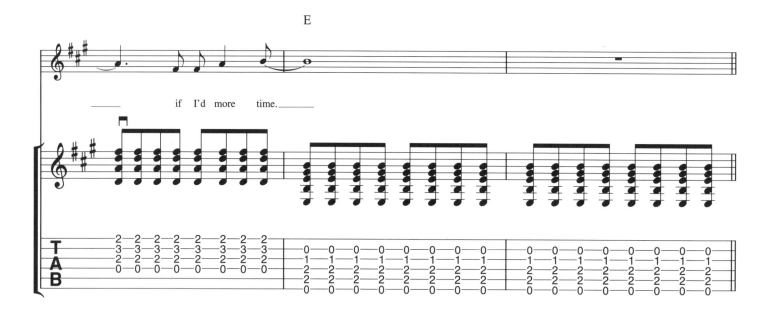

if I'd more time._____

Chorus:

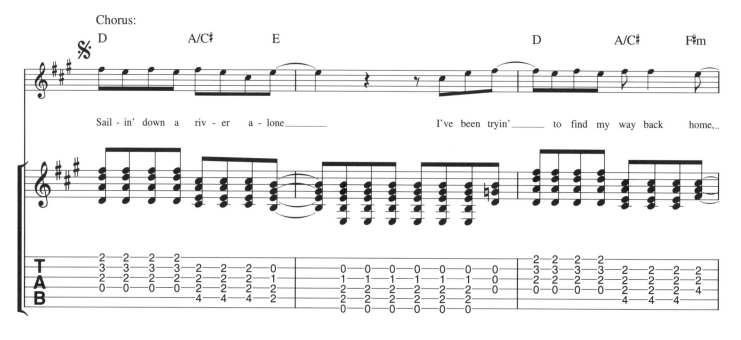

Sail - in' down a riv - er a - lone_____ I've been tryin'_____ to find my way back home,_

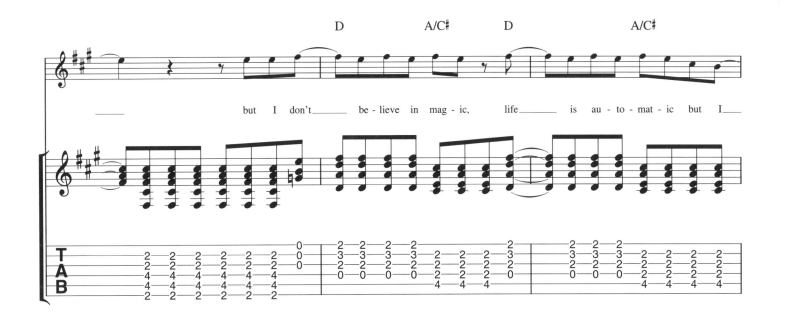

but I don't_____ be - lieve in mag - ic, life_____ is au - to - mat - ic but I_____

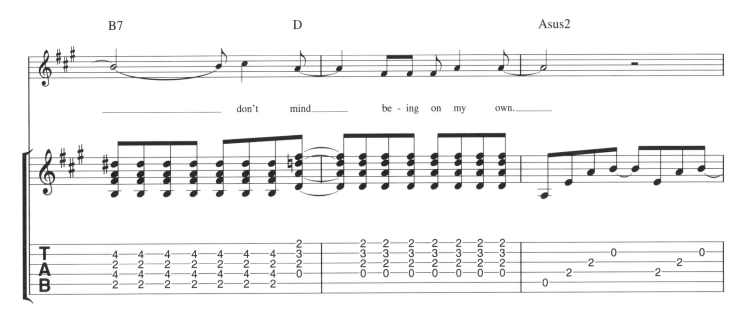

_____ don't mind_____ be - ing on my own._____

No I_____ don't mind_____ be - ing on my own.____

On (𝄋): I said that

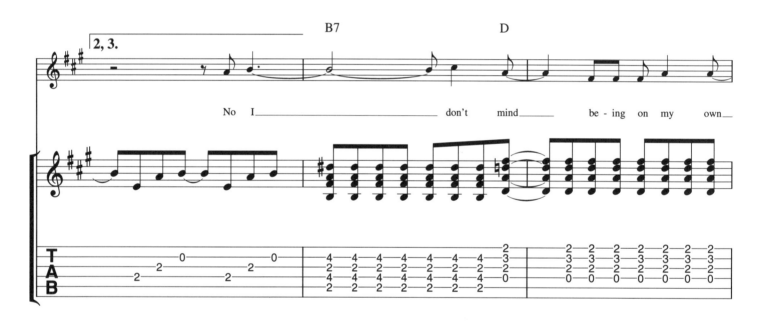

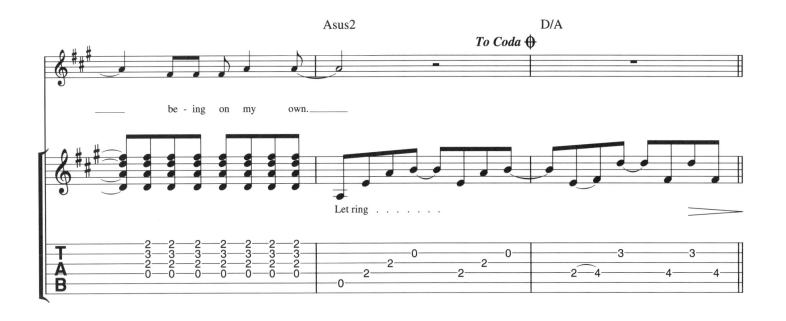

be - ing on my own.

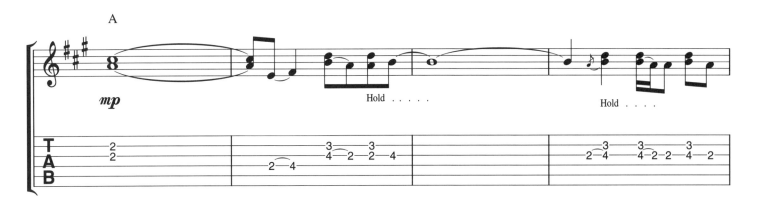

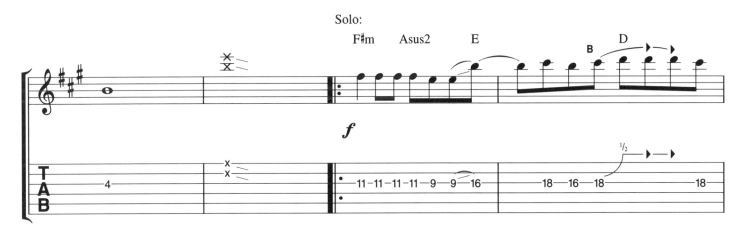

Solo:

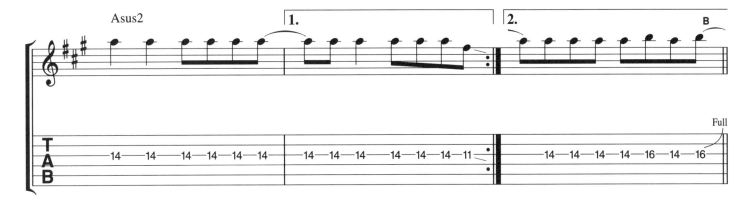

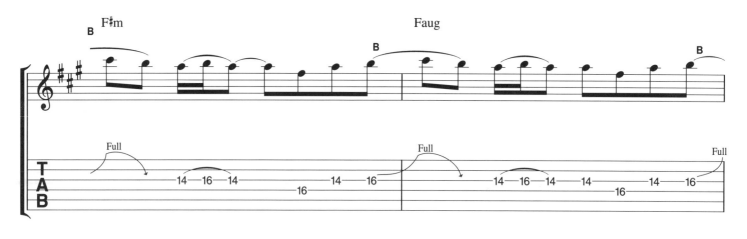

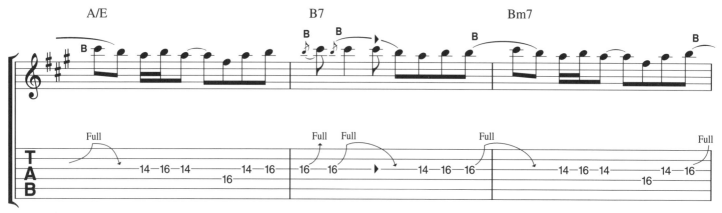

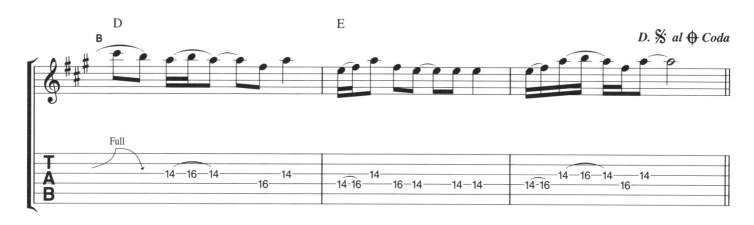

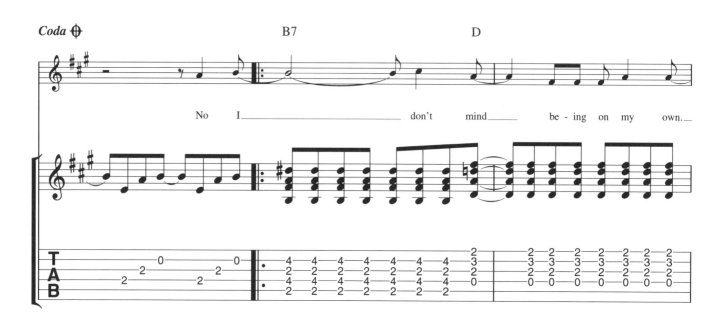

No I _____ don't mind _____ be - ing on my own. _____

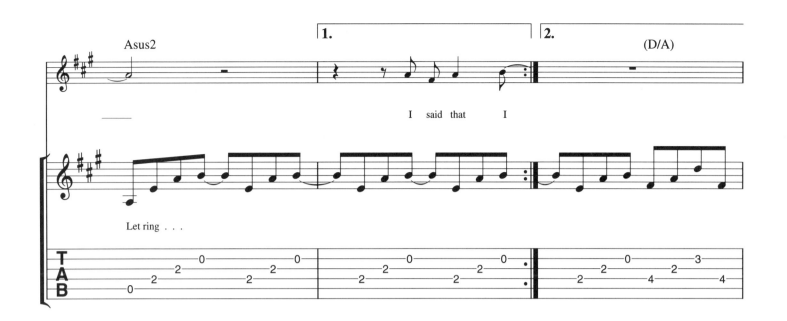

I said that I

Let ring . . .

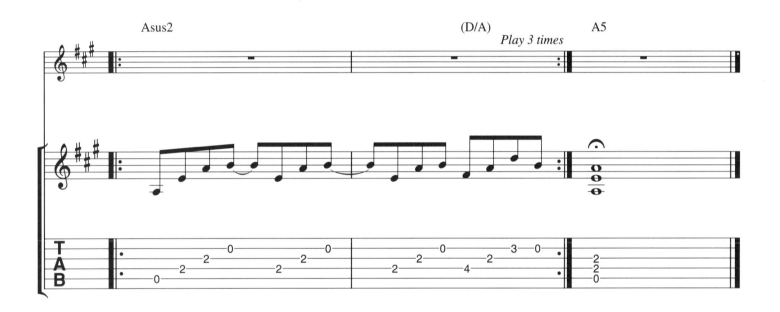

Play 3 times

ROCKIN' CHAIR

WORDS & MUSIC BY NOEL GALLAGHER & CHRIS GRIFFITHS

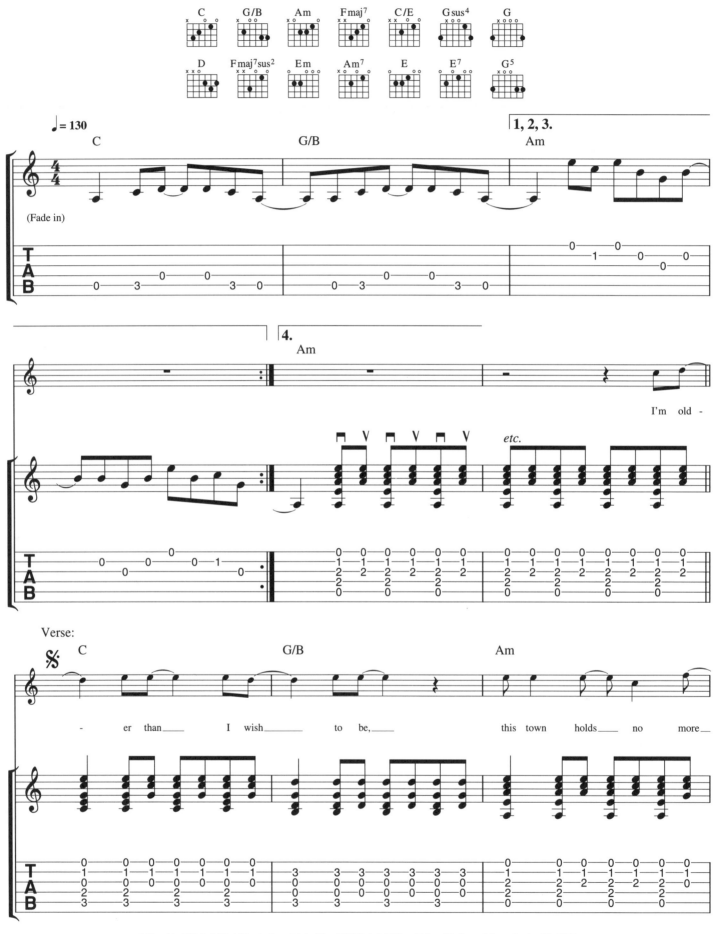

66

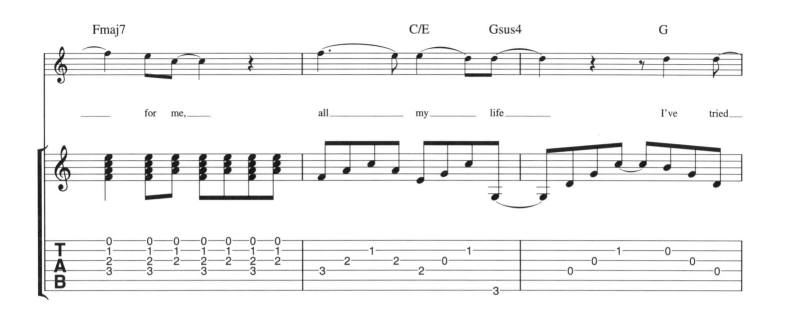

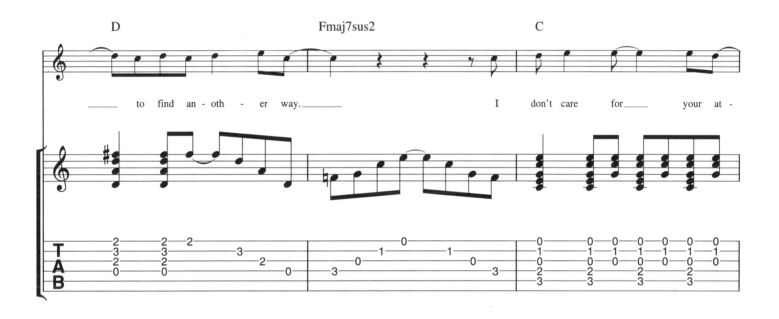

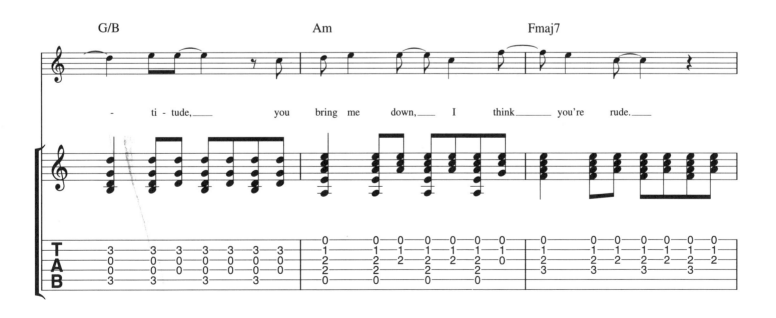

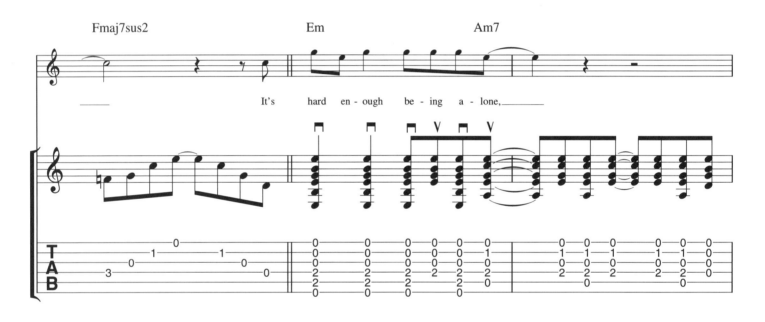

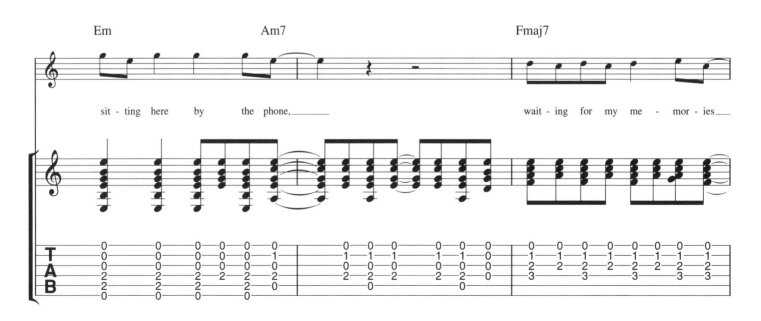

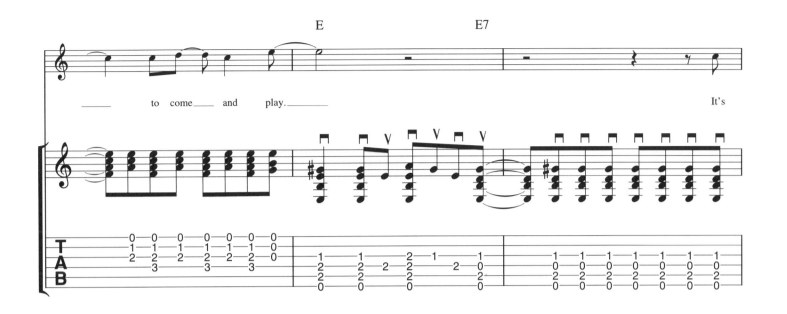

to come___ and play.___   It's

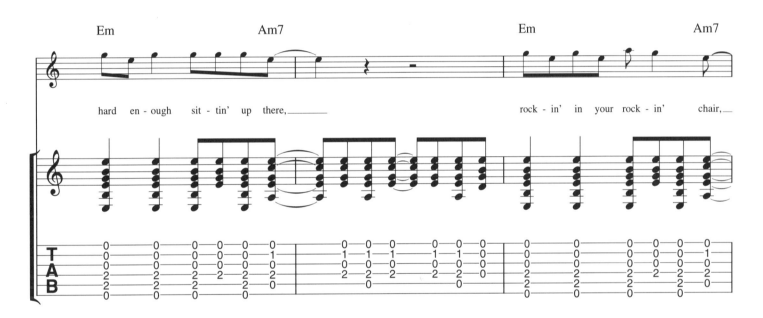

hard en - ough sit - tin' up there,___   rock - in' in your rock - in'   chair,___

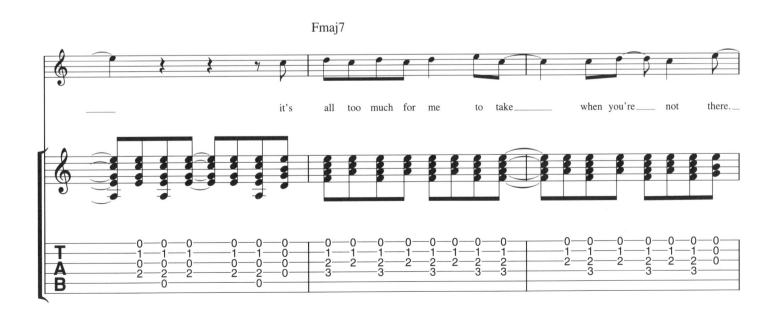

___   it's   all too much for me   to take___ when you're___ not   there.___

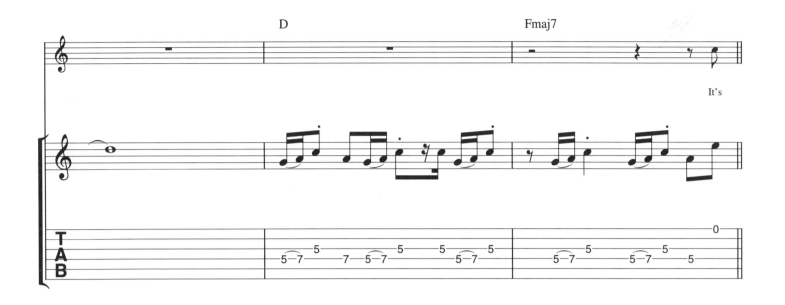

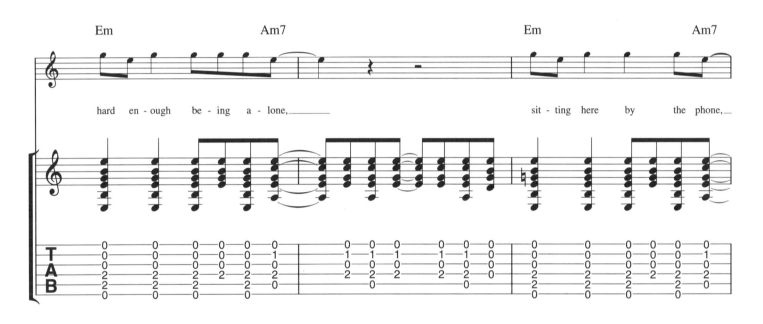

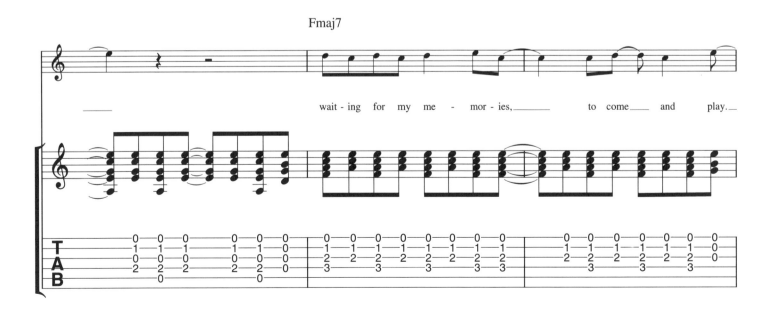

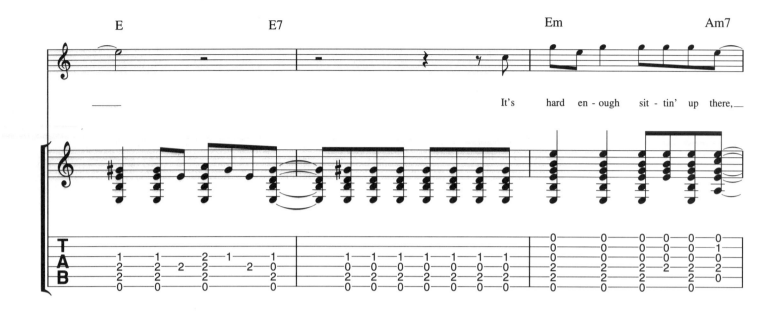

It's hard en-ough sit-tin' up there,

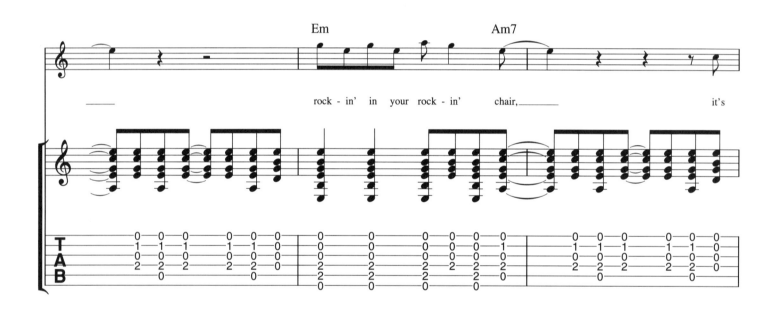

rock-in' in your rock-in' chair,_____ it's

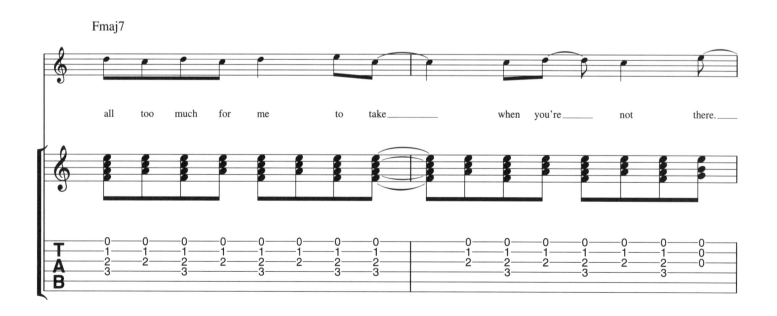

all too much for me to take_____ when you're_____ not there._____

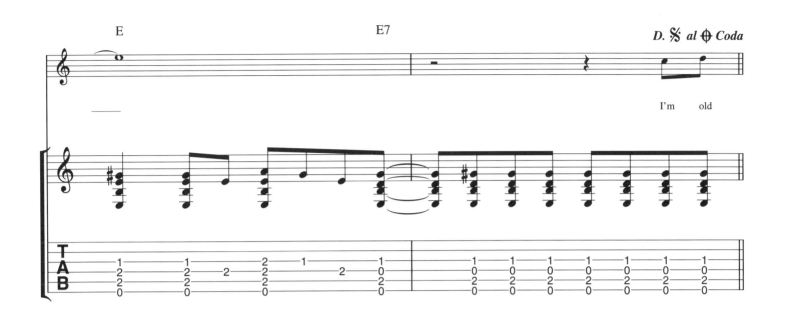

I'm   old

Hold . .

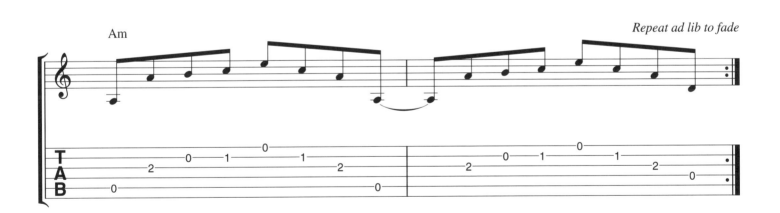

HALF THE WORLD AWAY

WORDS & MUSIC BY NOEL GALLAGHER

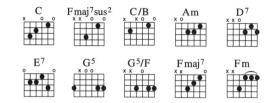

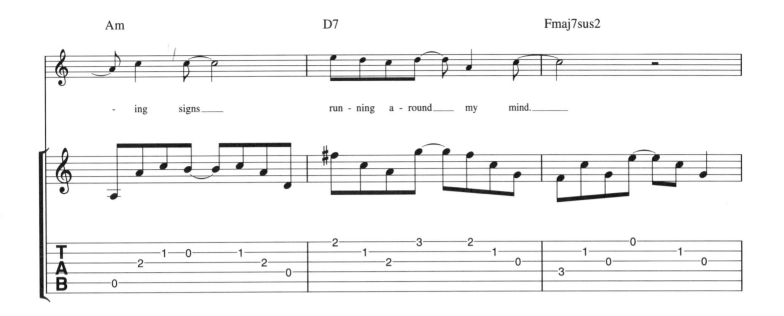

- ing signs____ run - ning a - round____ my mind.____

And when I leave this is - land, I'll book my - self____ in - to a soul____

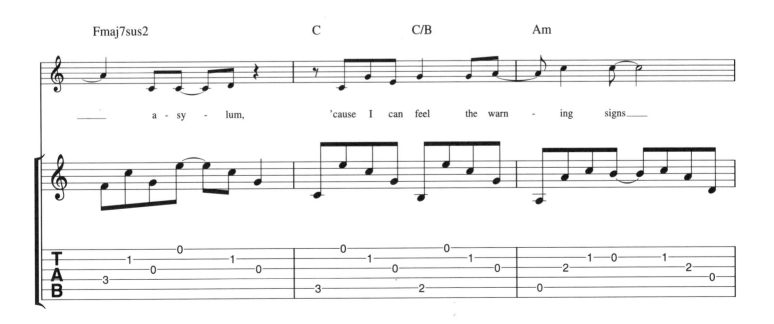

____ a - sy - lum, 'cause I can feel the warn - ing signs____

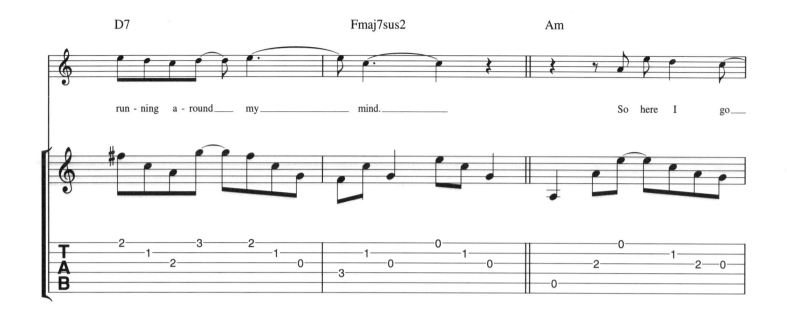

run - ning a - round___ my_____ mind._____   So here I go___

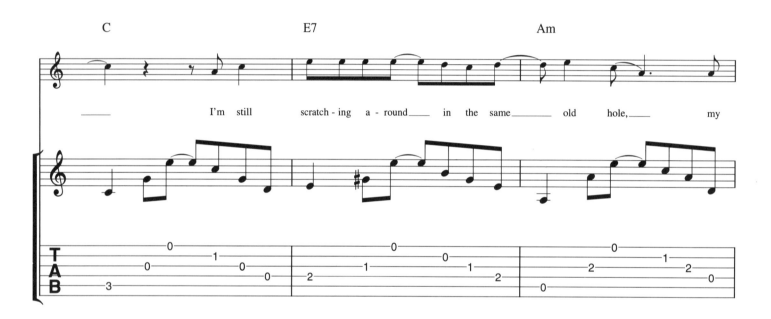

___ I'm still   scratch - ing a - round___ in the same___ old hole,___ my

bo - dy feels young___ but my mind_____ is ve - ry   old._____

So what do you say,_____ you can't

give me the dreams____ that are mine_____ a - ny - way,____ you're half____ the world a - way,____

half____ the world a - way,_____

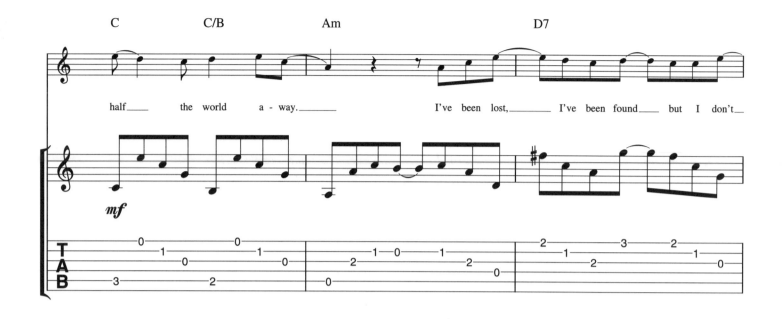

half ___ the world a - way. ___ I've been lost, ___ I've been found ___ but I don't ___

1.

Fmaj7sus2

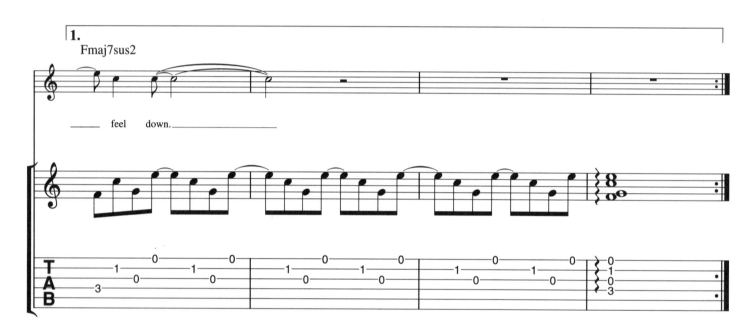

___ feel down. ___

2.

Fmaj7sus2

___ feel down. ___ No I don't ___ feel down, ___ no I don't ___

feel   down.

Repeat to fade

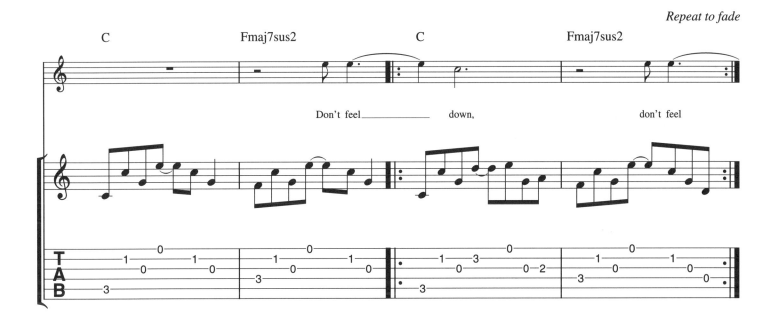

C   Fmaj7sus2   C   Fmaj7sus2

Don't feel _____ down,   don't feel

Verse 2:   And when I leave this planet
                  You know I'd stay but I just can't stand it
                  And I can feel the warning signs
                  Running around my mind.

                  And if I could leave this spirit
                  I'd find me a hole and I'll live in it
                  And I can feel the warning signs
                  Running around my mind.

(IT'S GOOD) TO BE FREE

WORDS & MUSIC BY NOEL GALLAGHER

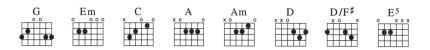

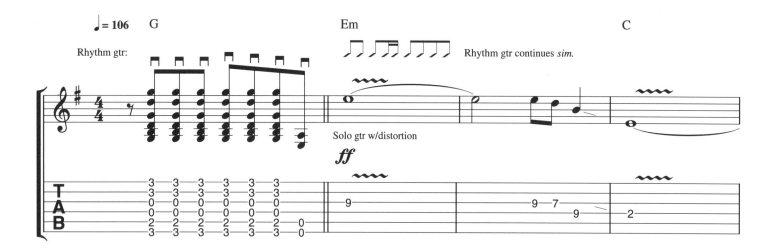

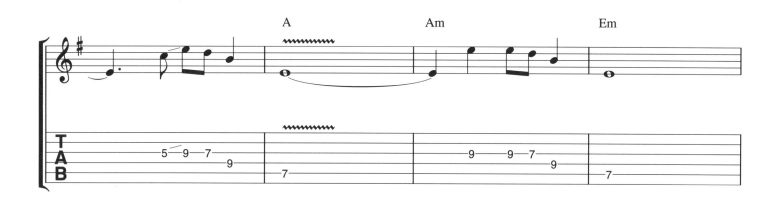

Verse:

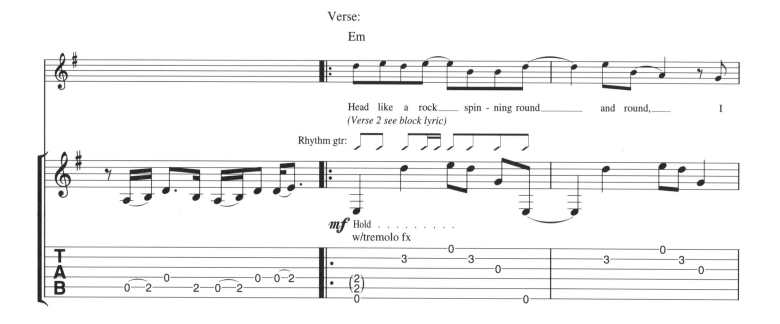

Head like a rock___ spin - ning round___ and round,___ I
(Verse 2 see block lyric)

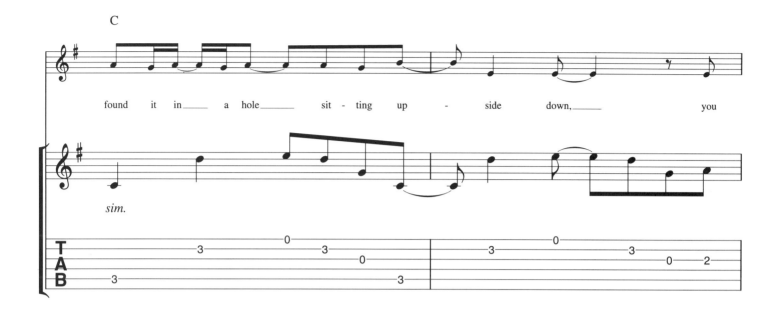

found it in___ a hole___ sit - ting up - side down,___ you

A

point your fin - ger at___ me   but I don't   be - lieve.___

Hold . . . . . .

Em   Em

Paint me a wish___ on a vel -

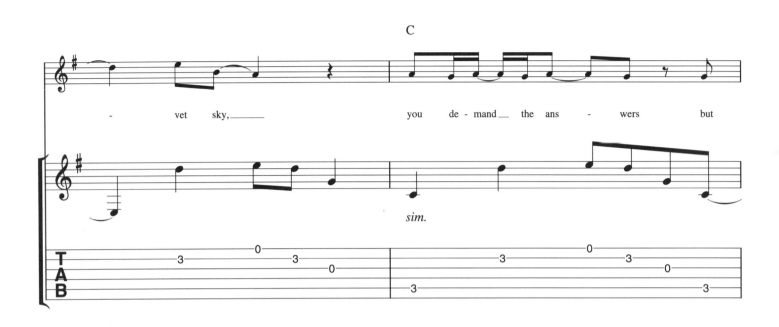

-vet sky,_____ you de - mand__ the ans - wers but

sim.

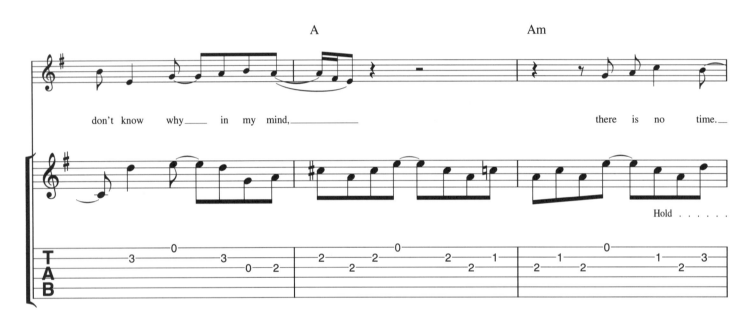

don't know why____ in my mind,_____ there is no time.__

Hold . . . . . .

_____ The

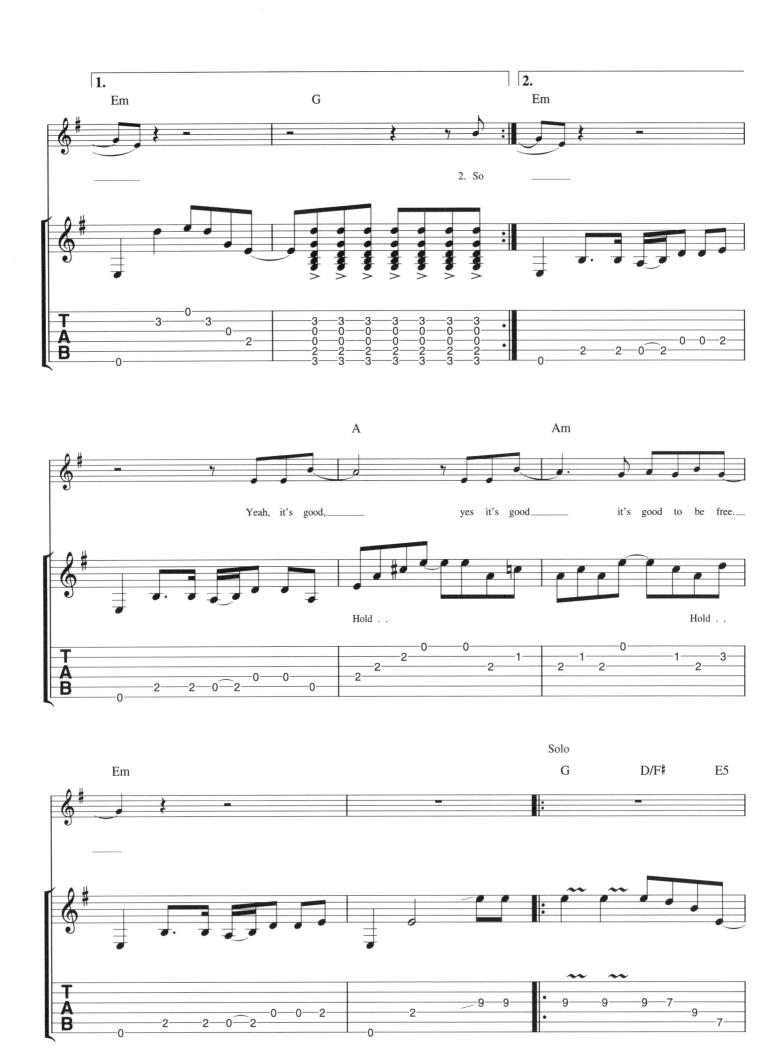

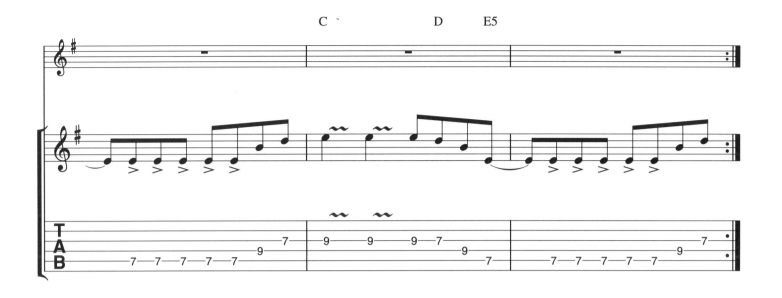

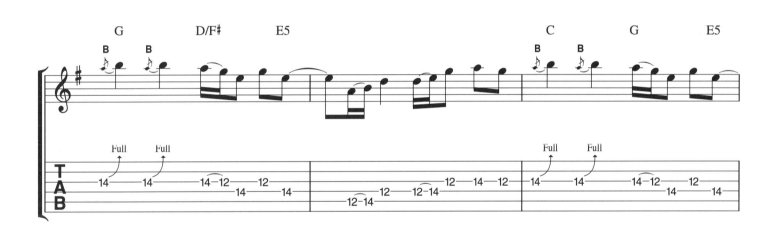

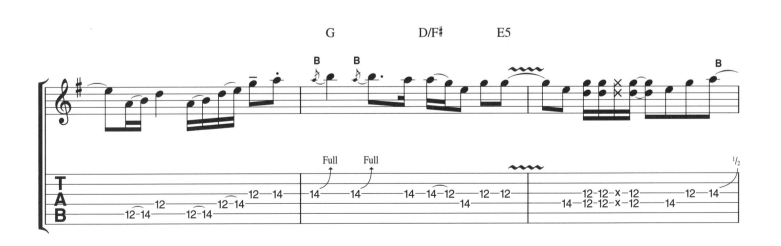

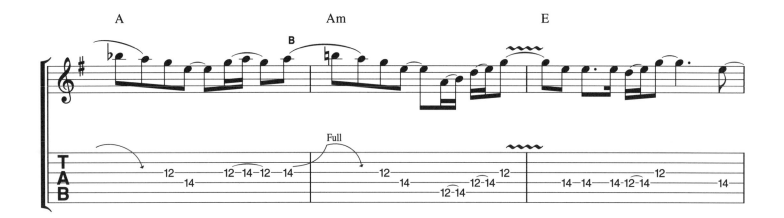

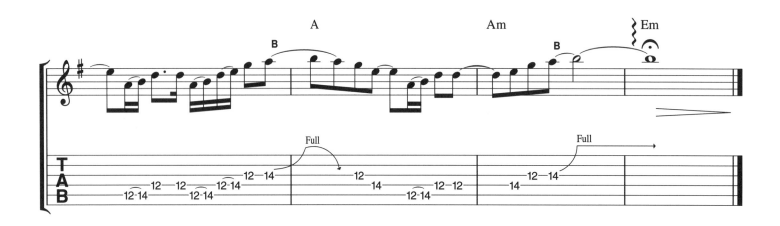

Verse 2:
So what would you say if I said to you
It's not in what you say, it's in what you do
You point the finger at me
But I don't believe.

Bring it on home to where we found
My head is like a rock sitting upside down
In my mind
There is no time.

STAY YOUNG

WORDS & MUSIC BY NOEL GALLAGHER

just what we are.

94

HEADSHRINKER

WORDS & MUSIC BY NOEL GALLAGHER

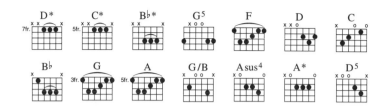

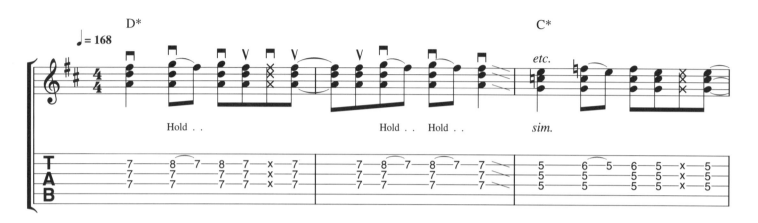

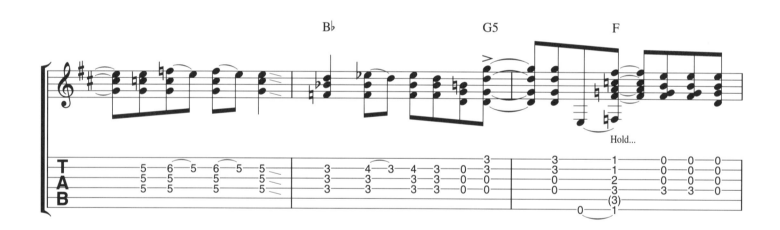

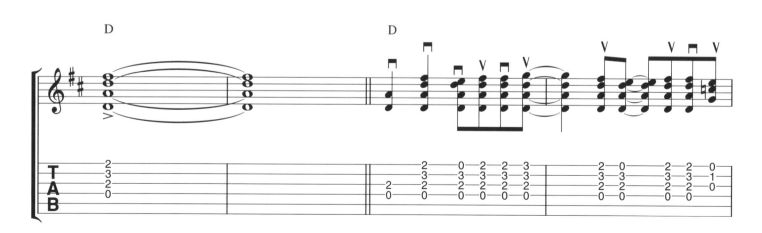

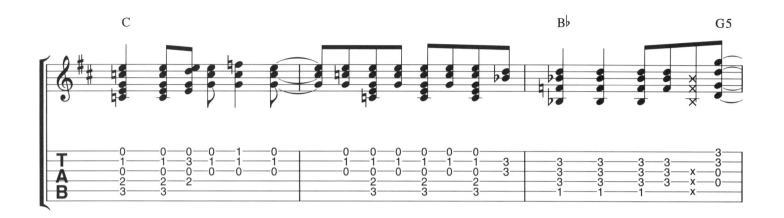

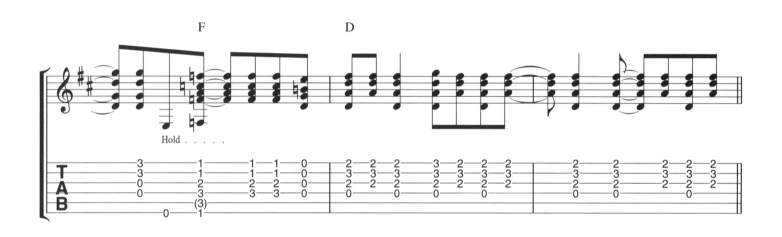

Verse:

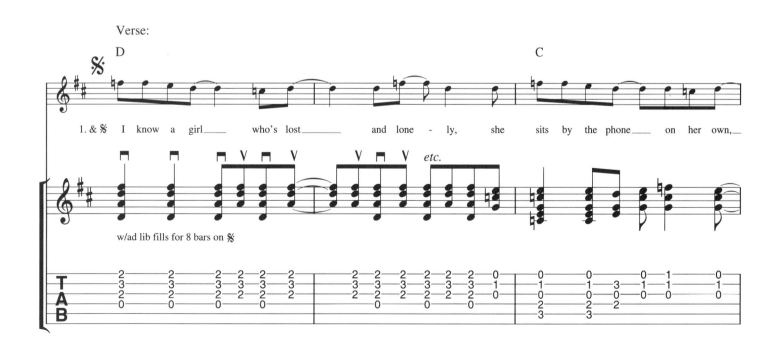

1. & % I know a girl who's lost and lone - ly, she sits by the phone on her own,

w/ad lib fills for 8 bars on %

but the phone_____ don't ring_____ and the birds_____ don't sing_____ in her

Hold . .

tree.   She lost her-self_____ in a haze_____

_____ of pi - ty   and   does - n't know where_____   to run,   she's a head-

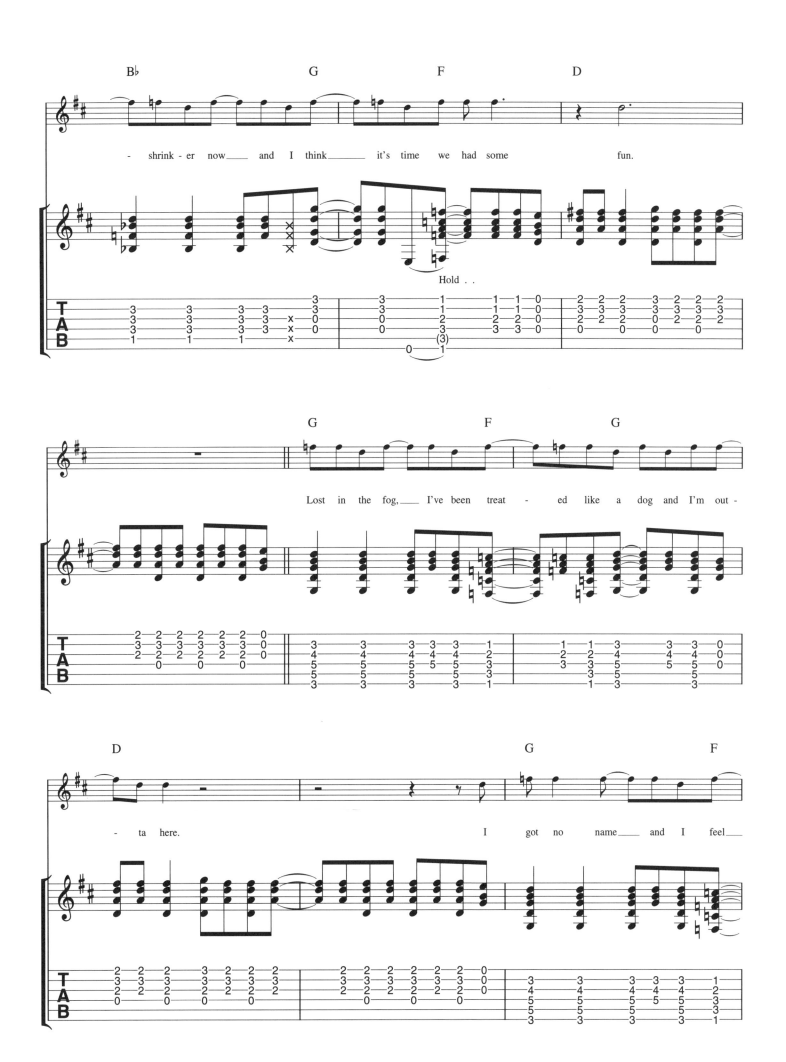

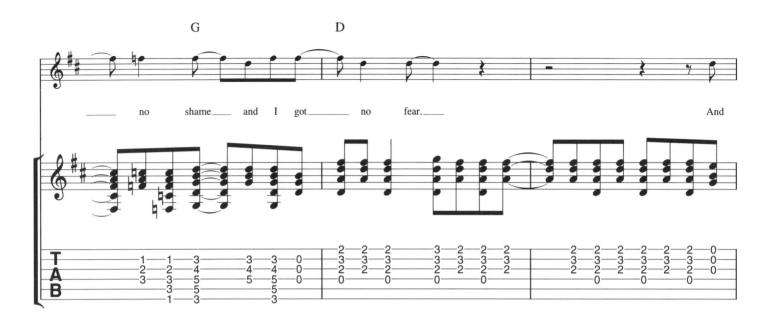

no shame____ and I got____ no fear.____ And

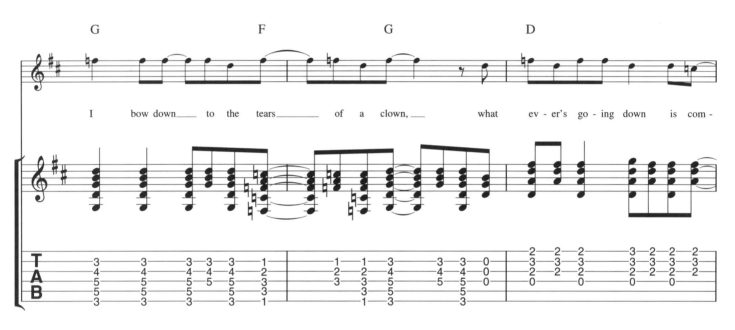

I bow down____ to the tears____ of a clown, ____ what ev - er's go - ing down is com -

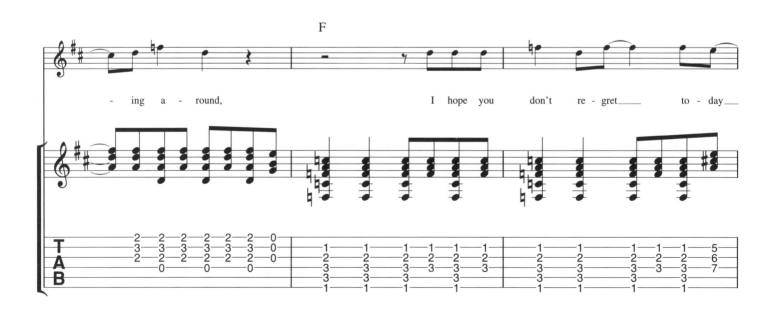

- ing a - round, I hope you don't re - gret____ to - day____

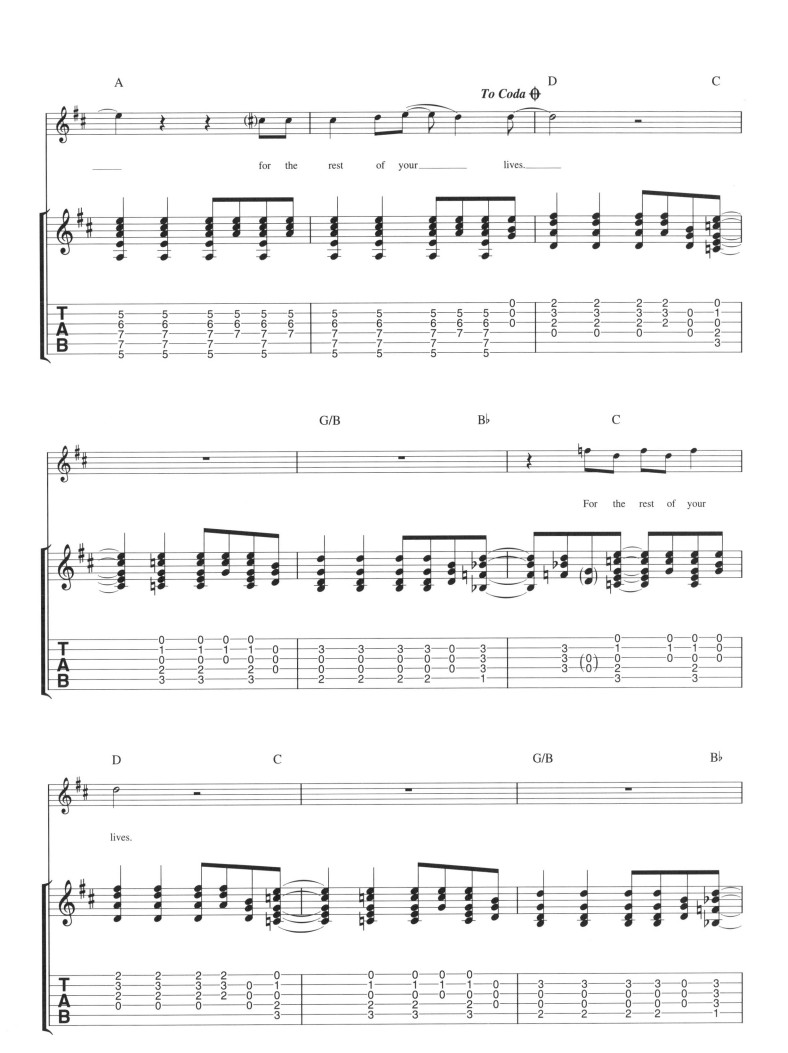

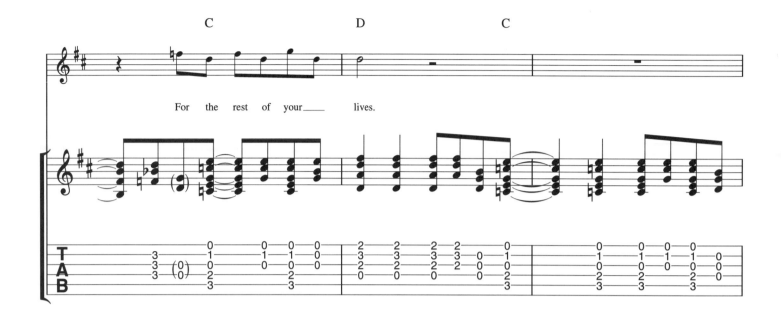

For the rest of your___ lives.

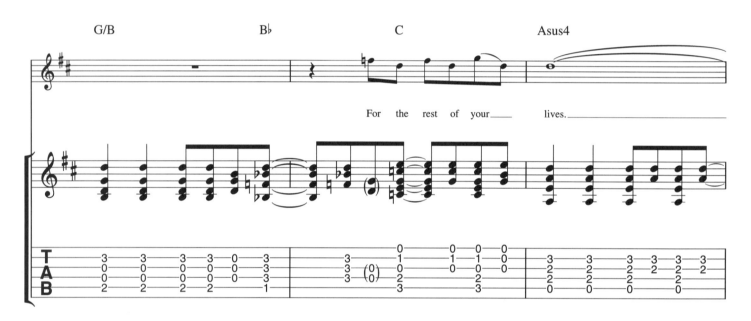

For the rest of your___ lives.___

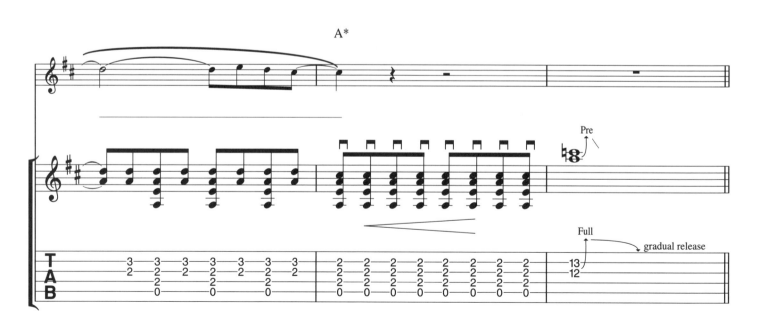

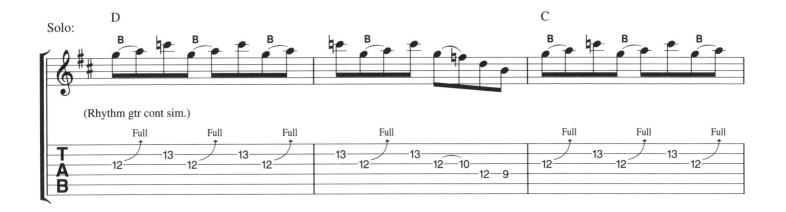

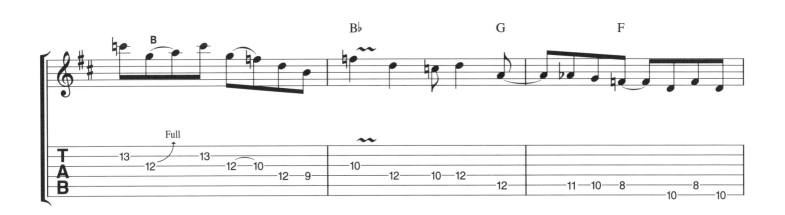

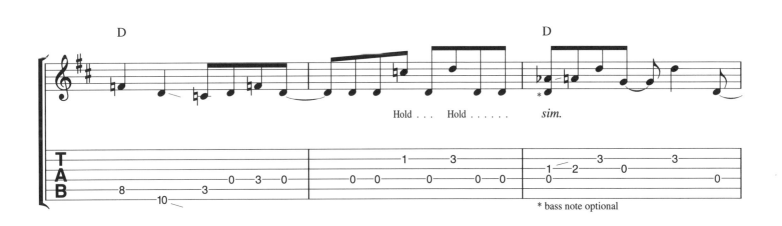

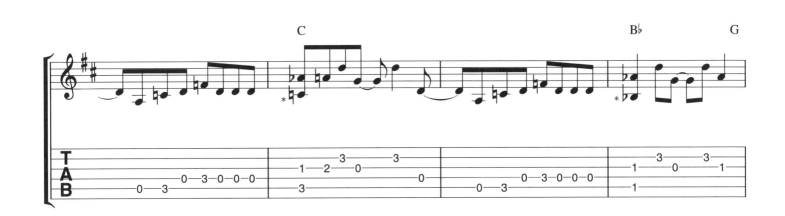

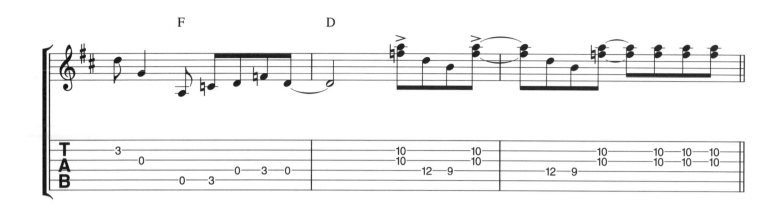

Lost in the fog,___ I've been treat - ed like a dog and I'm out - ta here.

I got no name___ and I feel___ no shame___ and I got___

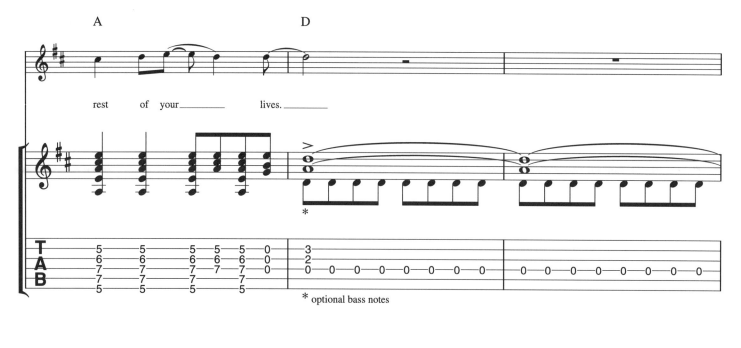

rest   of   your_____ lives. _____

* optional bass notes

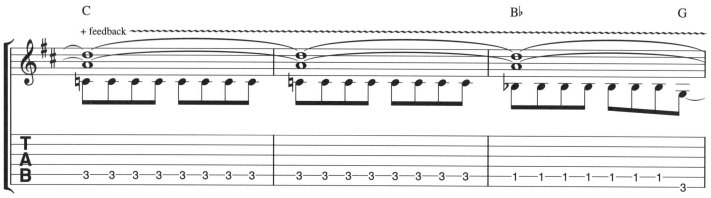

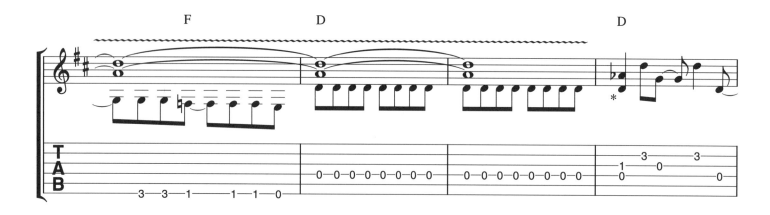

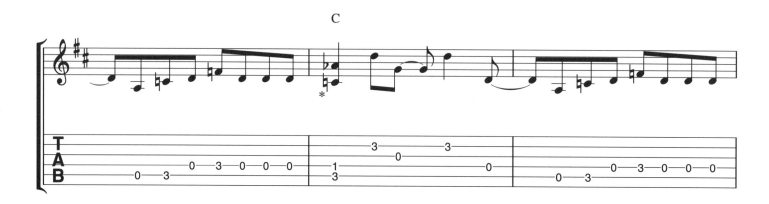

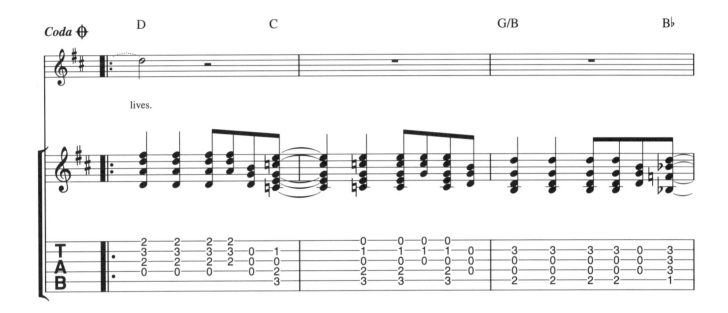

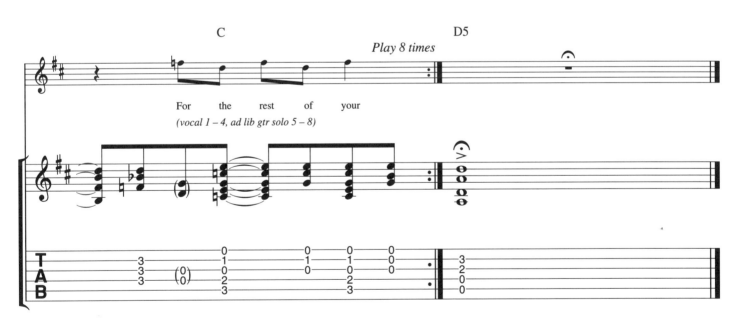

THE MASTERPLAN

WORDS & MUSIC BY NOEL GALLAGHER

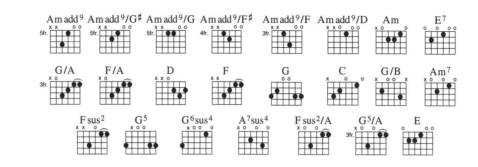

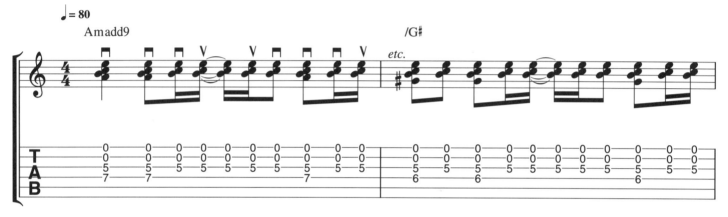

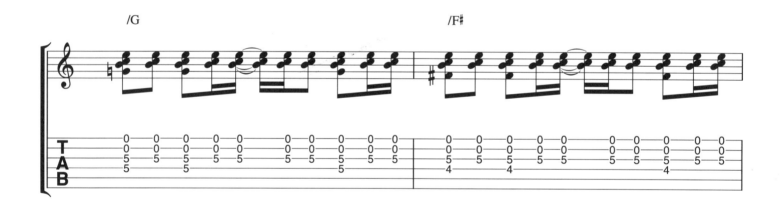

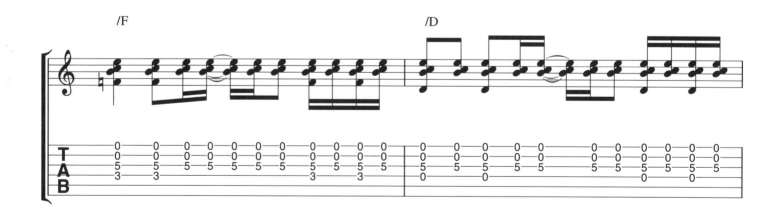

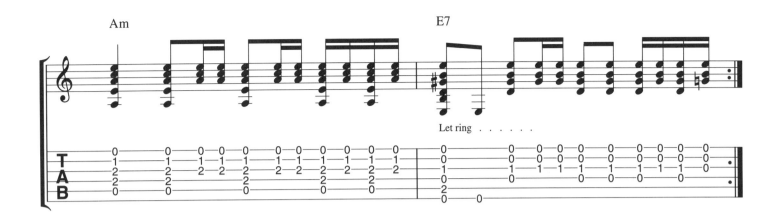

Verse:

1. Take the time___ to make___ some sense of what you want___ to say___ and
(Verse 2 see block lyric)

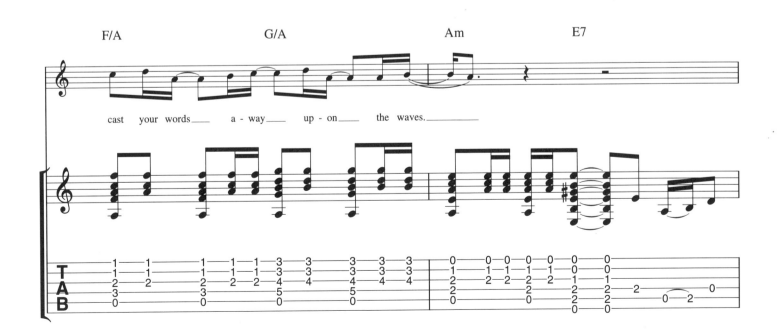

cast your words___ a - way___ up - on___ the waves.___

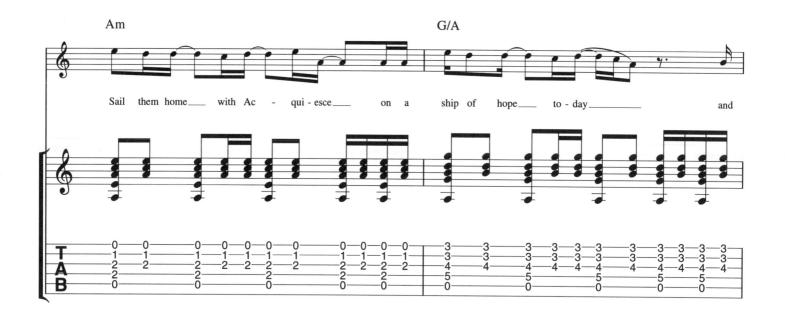

Sail them home___ with Ac - qui - esce___ on a ship of hope___ to - day___ and

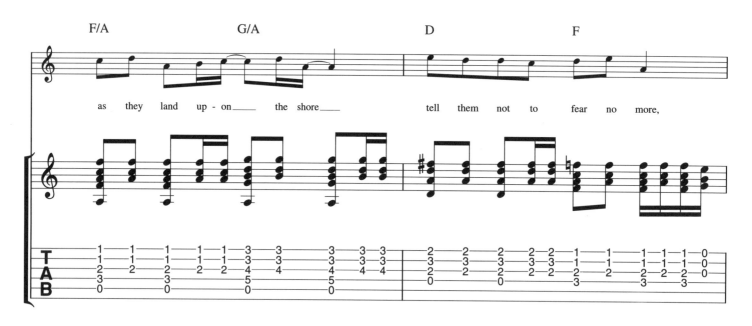

as they land up - on___ the shore___ tell them not to fear no more,

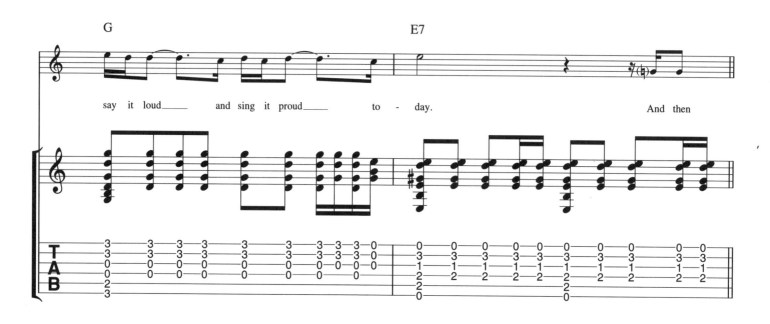

say it loud___ and sing it proud___ to - day. And then

Chorus:

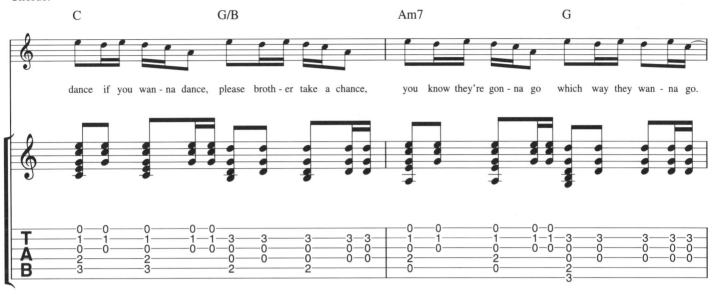

dance if you wan - na dance, please broth - er take a chance, you know they're gon - na go which way they wan - na go.

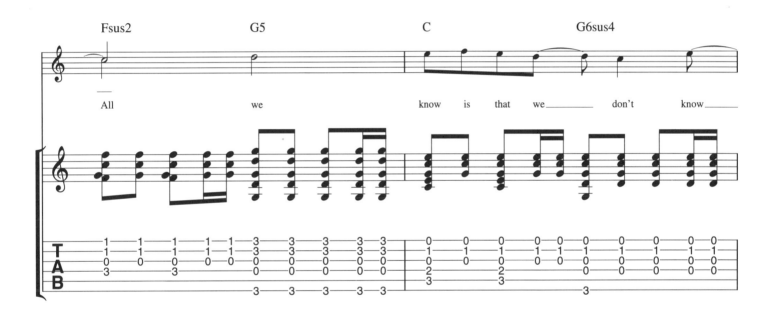

All we know is that we_____ don't know_____

_____ how it's gon - na be, please broth - er let it be. Life on the oth - er hand won't make us un - der - stand,_____

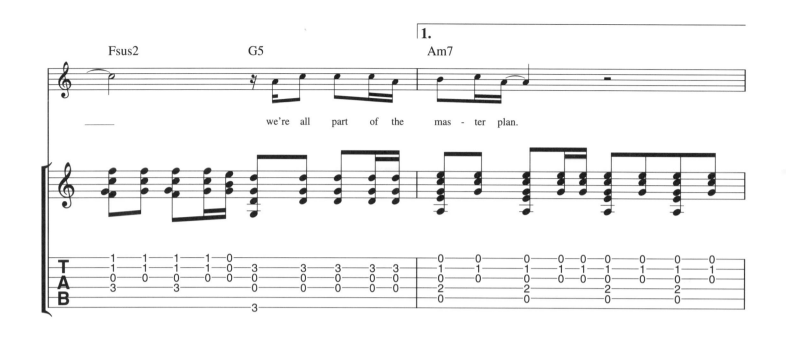

we're all part of the mas - ter plan.

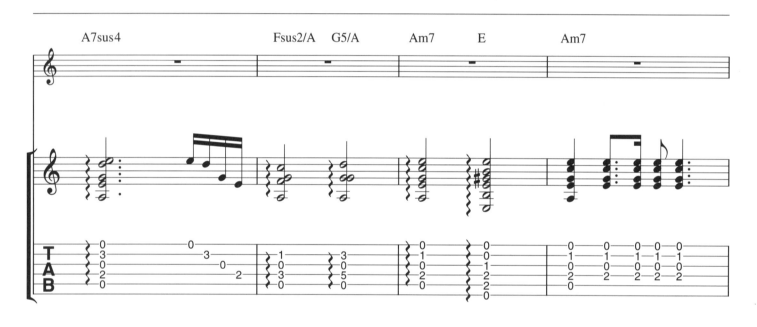

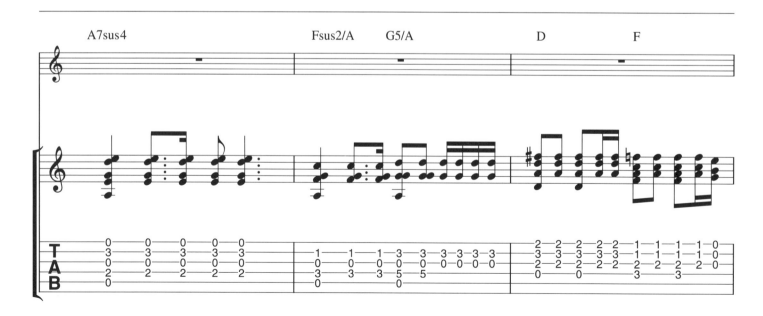

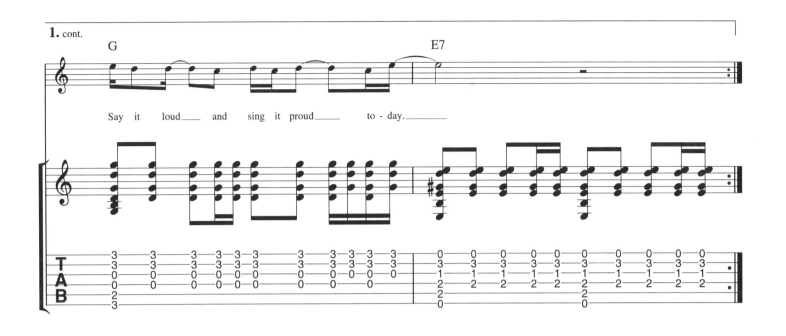

Say it loud___ and sing it proud____ to - day.____

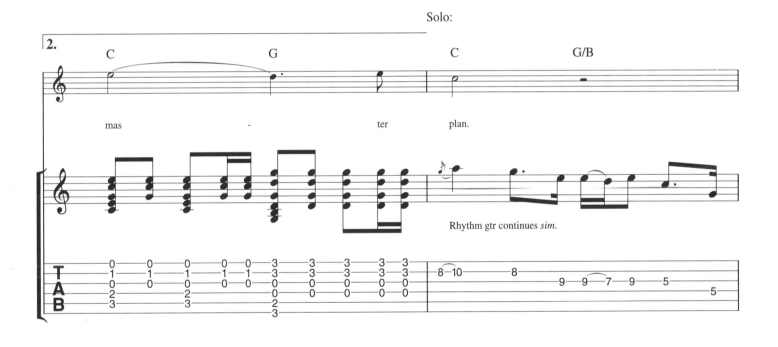

mas - ter plan.

Solo:

Rhythm gtr continues *sim.*

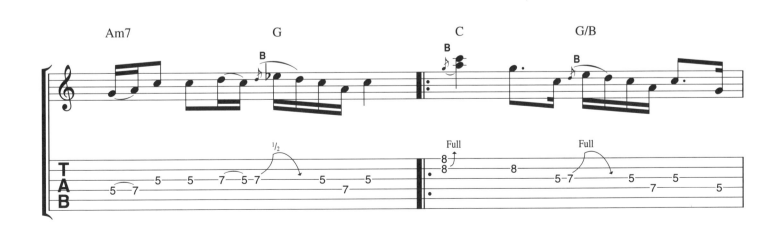

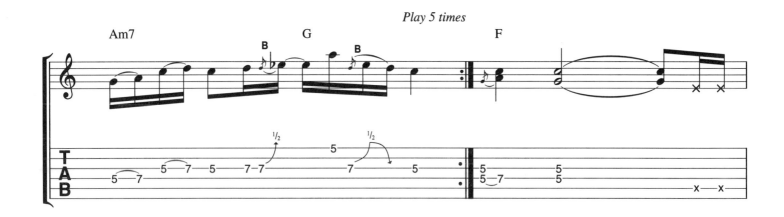

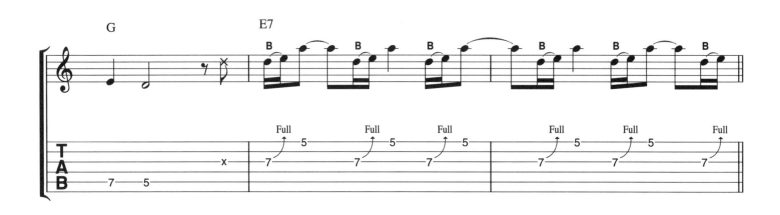

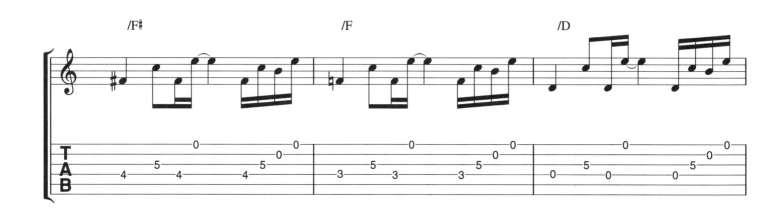

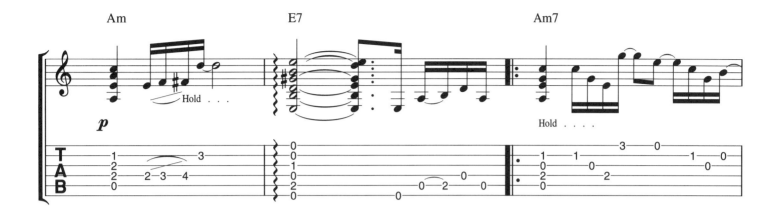

Play 3 times

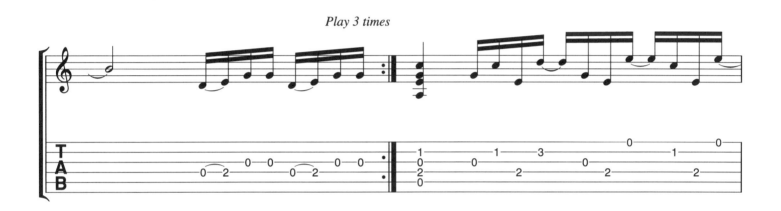

Verse 2:   I'm not saying right is wrong
            It's up to us to make
            The best of all the things that come our way.
            'Cos everything that's been has passed
            The answer's in the looking glass
            There's four and twenty million doors
            On life's endless corridor
            Say it loud and sing it proud today.

            Will dance if they want to dance
            Please brother take a chance . . . *etc.*

PRÉSENTATION DE LA TABLATURE DE GUITARE

Il existe trois façons différentes de noter la musique pour guitare : à l'aide d'une portée musicale, de tablatures ou de barres rythmiques

Les BARRES RYTHMIQUES sont indiquées au-dessus de la portée. Jouez les accords dans le rythme indiqué. Les notes rondes indiquent des notes réciles.

La PORTÉE MUSICALE indique les notes et rythmes et est divisée en mesures. Cette division est représentée par des lignes. Les notes sont : do, ré, mi, fa, sol, la, si.

La PORTÉE EN TABLATURE est une représentation graphique des touches de guitare. Chaque ligne horizontale correspond à une corde et chaque chiffre correspond à une case.

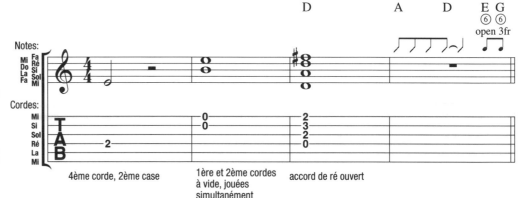

4ème corde, 2ème case   1ère et 2ème cordes à vide, jouées simultanément   accord de ré ouvert

Notation Spéciale De Guitare : Définitions

TIRÉ DEMI-TON : Jouez la note et tirez la corde afin d'élever la note d'un demi-ton (étape à moitié).

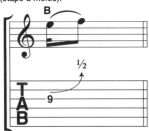

TIRÉ PLEIN : Jouez la note et tirez la corde afin d'élever la note d'un ton entier (étape entière).

TIRÉ D'AGRÉMENT : Jouez la note et tirez la corde comme indiqué. Jouez la première note aussi vite que possible.

TIRÉ QUART DE TON : Jouez la note et tirez la corde afin d'élever la note d'un quart de ton.

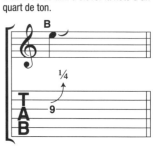

TIRÉ ET LÂCHÉ : Jouez la note et tirez la corde comme indiqué, puis relâchez, afin d'obtenir de nouveau la note de départ.

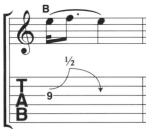

TIRÉ ET REJOUÉ : Jouez la note et tirez la corde comme indiqué puis rejouez la corde où le symbole apparaît.

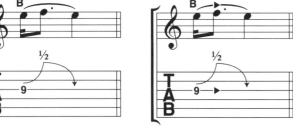

PRÉ-TIRÉ : Tirez la corde comme indiqué puis jouez cette note.

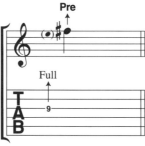

PRÉ-TIRÉ ET LÂCHÉ : Tirez la corde comme indiqué. Jouez la note puis relâchez la corde afin d'obtenir le ton de départ.

HAMMER-ON: Jouez la première note (plus basse) avec un doigt puis jouez la note plus haute sur la même corde avec un autre doigt, sur le manche mais sans vous servir du médiator.

PULL-OFF: Positionnez deux doigts sur les notes à jouer. Jouez la première note et sans vous servir du médiator, dégagez un doigt pour obtenir la deuxième note, plus basse.

GLISSANDO : Jouez la première note puis faites glisser le doigt le long du manche pour obtenir la seconde note qui, elle, n'est pas jouée.

GLISSANDO ET REJOUÉ : Identique au glissando à ceci près que la seconde note est jouée.

HARMONIQUES NATURELLES : Jouez la note tandis qu'un doigt effleure la corde sur le manche correspondant à la case indiquée.

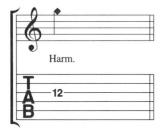

PICK SCRAPE (SCRATCH) : On fait glisser le médiator le long de la corde, ce qui produit un son éraillé.

ÉTOUFFÉ DE LA PAUME : La note est partiellement étouffée par la main (celle qui se sert du médiator). Elle effleure la (les) corde(s) juste au-dessus du chevalet.

CORDES ÉTOUFFÉES : Un effet de percussion produit en posant à plat la main sur le manche sans relâcher, puis en jouant les cordes avec le médiator.

NOTE : La vitesse des tirés est indiquée par la notation musicale et le tempo.

ERLÄUTERUNG ZUR TABULATURSCHREIBWEISE

Es gibt drei Möglichkeiten, Gitarrenmusik zu notieren: im klassichen Notensystem, in Tabulaturform oder als rhythmische Akzente

RHYTHMISCHE AKZENTE werden über dem Notensystem notiert. Geschlagene Akkorde werden rhythmisch dargestellt. Ausgeschriebene Noten stellen Einzeltöne dar.

Im **NOTENSYSTEM** werden Tonhöhe und rhythmischer Verlauf festgelegt; es ist durch Taktstriche in Takte unterteilt. Die Töne werden nach den ersten acht Buchstaben des Alphabets benannt.
Beachte: "B" in der anglo-amerikanischen Schreibweise entspricht dem deutschen "H"!

DIE TABULATUR ist die optische Darstellung des Gitarrengriffbrettes. Jeder horizontalen Linie ist eine bestimmte Saite zugeordnet, jede Zahl bezeichnet einen Bund.

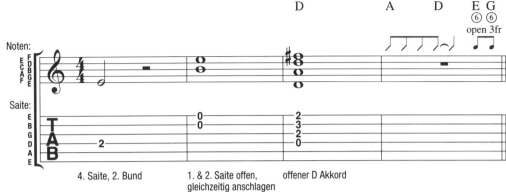

4. Saite, 2. Bund   1. & 2. Saite offen, gleichzeitig anschlagen   offener D Akkord

Erklärungen zur speziellen Gitarennotation

HALBTON-ZIEHER: Spiele die Note und ziehe dann um einen Halbton höher (Halbtonschritt).

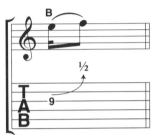

GANZTON-ZIEHER: Spiele die Note und ziehe dann einen Ganzton höher (Ganztonschritt).

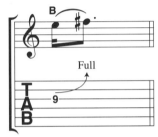

ZIEHER MIT VORSCHLAG: Spiele die Note und ziehe wie notiert. Spiele die erste Note so schnell wie möglich.

VIERTELTON-ZIEHER: Spiele die Note und ziehe dann einen Viertelton höher (Vierteltonschritt).

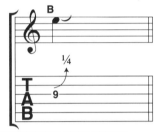

ZIEHEN UND ZURÜCKGLEITEN: Spiele die Note und ziehe wie notiert; lasse den Finger dann in die Ausgangsposition zurückgleiten. Dabei wird nur die erste Note angeschlagen.

ZIEHEN UND NOCHMALIGES ANSCHLAGEN: Spiele die Note und ziehe wie notiert, schlage die Saite neu an, wenn das Symbol "►" erscheint und lasse den Finger dann zurückgleiten.

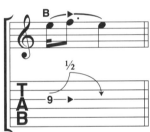

ZIEHER VOR DEM ANSCHLAGEN: Ziehe zuerst die Note wie notiert; schlage die Note dann an.

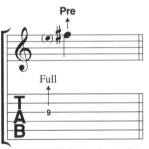

ZIEHER VOR DEM ANSCHLAGEN MIT ZURÜCKGLEITEN: Ziehe die Note wie notiert; schlage die Note dann an und lasse den Finger auf die Ausgangslage zurückgleiten.

AUFSCHLAGTECHNIK: Schlage die erste (tiefere) Note an; die höhere Note (auf der selben Saite) erklingt durch kräftiges Aufschlagen mit einem anderen Finger der Griffhand.

ABZIEHTECHNIK: Setze beide Finger auf die zu spielenden Noten und schlage die erste Note an. Ziehe dann (ohne nochmals anzuschlagen) den oberen Finger der Griffhand seitlich - abwärts ab, um die zweite (tiefere) Note zum klingen zu bringen.

GLISSANDOTECHNIK: Schlage die erste Note an und rutsche dann mit dem selben Finger der Griffhand aufwärts oder abwärts zur zweiten Note. Die zweite Note wird nicht angeschlagen.

GLISSANDOTECHNIK MIT NACHFOLGENDEM ANSCHLAG: Gleiche Technik wie das gebundene Glissando, jedoch wird die zweite Note angeschlagen.

NATÜRLICHES FLAGEOLETT: Berühre die Saite über dem angegebenen Bund leicht mit einem Finger der Griffhand. Schlage die Saite an und lasse sie frei schwingen.

PICK SCRAPE: Fahre mit dem Plektrum nach unten über die Saiten - klappt am besten bei umsponnenen Saiten.

DÄMPFEN MIT DER SCHLAGHAND: Lege die Schlaghand oberhalb der Brücke leicht auf die Saite(n).

DÄMPFEN MIT DER GRIFFHAND: Du erreichst einen percussiven Sound, indem du die Griffhand leicht über die Saiten legst (ohne diese herunterzudrücken) und dann mit der Schlaghand anschlägst.

AMMERKUNG: Das Tempo der Zieher und Glissandos ist abhängig von der rhythmischen Notation und dem Grundtempo.

SPIEGAZIONI DI TABLATURA PER CHITARRA

La musica per chitarra può essere annotata in tre diversi modi: sul pentagramma, in tablatura e in taglio ritmico

IL TAGLIO RITMICO è scritto sopra il pentagramma. Percuotere le corde al ritmo indicato Le teste arrotondate delle note indicano note singole.

IL PENTAGRAMMA MUSICALE mostra toni e ritmo ed è divisa da linee in settori. I toni sono indicati con le prime sette lettere dell'alfabeto.

LA TABLATURA rappresenta graficamente la tastiera della chitarra. Ogni linea orizzontale rappresenta una corda, ed ogni corda rappresenta un tasto.

4° corda, 2° tasto   1° e 2° corda aperte,   accordo D aperto
                          suonate insieme

Definizioni Per Annotazioni Speciali Per Chitarra

SEMI-TONO CURVATO: percuotere la nota e curvare di un semitono (1/2 passo).

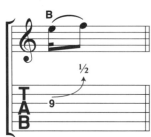

TONO CURVATO: Percuotere la nota e curvare di un tono (passo intero).

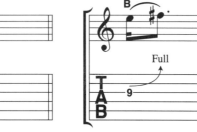

NOTA BREVE, CURVATA: percuotere la nota e curvare come indicato. Suonare la prima nota il più velocemente possibile.

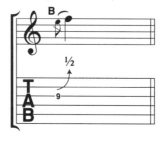

QUARTO DI TONO, CURVATO: Percuotere la nota e curvare di un quarto di passo.

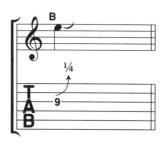

CURVA E LASCIA: Percuotere la nota e curvare come indicato, quindi rilasciare indietro alla nota originale.

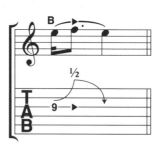

CURVA E RIPERCUOTI: Percuotere la nota e curvare come indicato poi ripercuotere la corda nel punto del simbolo.

PRE-CURVA: Curvare la nota come indicato e quindi percuoterla.

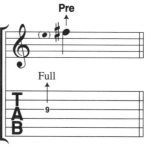

PRE-CURVA E RILASCIO: Curvare la nota come indicato. Colpire e rilasciare la nota indietro alla tonalità indicata.

MARTELLO-COLPISCI: Colpire la prima nota (in basso) con un dito; quindi suona la nota più alta (sulla stessa corda) con un altro dito, toccandola senza pizzicare.

TOGLIERE: Posizionare entrambe le dita sulla nota da suonare. Colpire la prima nota e, senza pizzicare, togliere le dita per suonare la seconda nota (più in basso).

LEGATO SCIVOLATO (GLISSATO): Colpire la prima nota e quindi far scivolare lo stesso dito della mano della tastiera su o giù alla seconda nota. La seconda nota non viene colpita.

CAMBIO SCIVOLATO (GLISSARE E RICOLPIRE): Uguale al legato - scivolato eccetto che viene colpita la seconda nota.

ARMONICA NATURALE: Colpire la nota mentre la mano della tastiera tocca leggermente la corda direttamente sopra il tasto indicato.

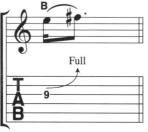

PIZZICA E GRAFFIA: Il limite del pizzicato è tirato su (o giù) lungo la corda, producendo un suono graffiante.

SORDINA CON IL PALMO: La nota è parzialmente attenuato dalla mano del pizzicato toccando la corda (le corde) appena prima del ponte.

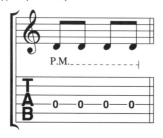

CORDE SMORZATE: Un suono di percussione viene prodotto appoggiando la mano della tastiera attraverso la corda (le corde) senza premere, e colpendole con la mano del pizzicato.

NOTA: La velocità di ogni curvatura è indicata dalle annotazioni musicali e dal tempo.